The Substance of Man

The Substance of Man

by *JEAN ROSTAND*
of the Académie française

TRANSLATED BY IRMA BRANDEIS

GREENWOOD PRESS, PUBLISHERS
WESTPORT, CONNECTICUT

The Library of Congress has catalogued this publication as follows:

Library of Congress Cataloging in Publication Data

Rostand, Jean, 1894–
    The substance of man.

    Translation of Pensées d'un biologiste and Carnets
d'un biologiste.
        I. Rostand, Jean, 1894–   Carnets d'un biologiste.
English. 1972. II. Title.
PQ2635.0815P4413 1972   574'.092'4   72-7509
    ISBN 0-8371-6517-2

THE SUBSTANCE OF MAN was originally published by Librairie Stock, Paris, as two separate volumes under the titles PENSÉES D'UN BIOLOGISTE and CARNETS D'UN BIOLOGISTE.

The translator would like to acknowledge the invaluable criticism and advice of Mr. Carl Morse.

Contents

A BIOLOGIST'S THOUGHTS   1

A BIOLOGIST'S NOTEBOOK   175

A Biologist's Thoughts

I

Where politics, morals, or philosophy are concerned, I view with suspicion the judgment of those who know nothing about their own composition.

Knowledge should come before dreaming.

The two infinites that Blaise Pascal trembled to think of are today the familiar ground of science. The infinite of bigness is the province of astronomers; that of smallness falls to the physicists. The biologist stands midway between; yet it is he who, without ever quitting the realm of living matter, comes in touch with the prodigious. Man has no need to plunge into the two Pascalian abysses in order to be appalled by what he is: let him merely scrutinize his own substance.

The number of hereditary combinations capable of arising from the union of two human beings is not less than several hundred trillions. A single couple could give rise to enough offspring—no two alike—to people several planets as vast as ours with their heterogeneous crowds. Every man has trillions of possible brothers.

To procreate, just as Novalis said of gambling, is to experiment with chance.

All human diversity results from the virtually infinite combinations of genes. All of us are formed of the same chromosomal dust; none of us has a single grain of it that he can claim as exclusively his own. It is our ensemble that belongs to us and makes our separate identities; we are an original mosaic of banal elements.

Everyone shares the gross stuff of his being with others; all men are essentially consubstantial.

Through his hereditary make-up each individual may lay claim to a basic originality. He is the only one of himself. "Nobody is my like," said Max Stirner; "my flesh is not their flesh, nor my thought their thought." And biologically, the fierce theoretician of *The Unique* could not have spoken more truly.

Even were the earth to last all those millions of centuries predicted by the astronomers, there is no apparent likelihood that the blind caprices of heredity would repeat any individual's precise combination of chromosomes and thus give him a second chance at life. Chance may have produced man—but it cannot make two identical examples.

So strong is the biologic singularity of the individual that a morsel of flesh from one man's body perishes when grafted on another's. Our humors are poisonous to our fellows.

Nietzsche spoke somewhere of writing with one's blood. Which would be to say, with one's chromosomes.

Fontenelle asked a charming question: "What can nature's secret possibly be for varying in so many ways so simple a thing as a face?" We know that secret now: it is the chromosomal law of distribution; and its mathematical simplicity would no doubt have delighted the author of *The Plurality of Worlds*.

Chance enters twice into the begetting of the germ from which the human individual emerges. It is chance that decides what hereditary portion is to be stationed in the maturing ovum when it expels its twenty-four chromosomes. It is chance, again, that determines which of the fertilizing elements is to penetrate the ovum. Each one of us was elected by a double caprice from among a whole disparate multitude, and each is certainly neither the worst nor the best that his parents could have begotten.

What inequality and what dissimilarity in the bewildering throng that a single human couple could engender! Offspring tall and short, blond and dark, handsome and ugly, weak and strong. Everything is possible: imperfection and excellence, doltishness and genius, monstrosities of both ends of the scale. Anything can be born of the mixing of two individuals. One may reasonably hope everything and fear anything from any human union. The most ordinary of couples is pregnant with the whole of humankind.

When Schopenhauer affirmed that man is attracted to the woman capable of bearing him the best offspring, the philosopher was simply unaware of the fact that two individuals are capable, at any moment, of engendering trillions of different children.

In the assortment of chromosomes we receive from each parent there are present all the necessary ingredients for making a complete creature. Thus every individual is essentially double. I have heard it said each man is several. The phase is inexact; *Homo duplex* is the biological verity.

If every human creature is two, four are involved in the begetting of a child. Biologically speaking, every couple is a *ménage à quatre*.

The infant is not his whole father plus his whole mother; he does not, as Hegel would have it, manifest "the living fusion of the couple." He is half of one plus half the other. The two beings that existed potentially in the two parental cells are mingled in him. Strange, and stirring to the imagination, this joining together by one's own life of two beings who, separately, never achieved existence at all, and whose synthesis we bring about. Each has his own face, character, soul. Perhaps both are quite unlike us. Possibly one of them is our superior. It must, indeed, sometimes occur that a man thus lodges his better within him.

We never bequeath more than half of ourselves, and our children do not carry us on by more than half. Immortality by means of offspring is only half an immortality. As Schopenhauer observed, the individual destroys himself in procreation as in death. In the chromosomal splitting of our germ cells, we divorce ourselves.

We pass half of ourselves on to our children, unavoidably; but when they, in turn, transmit a half of themselves to still other new beings, it is impossible to predict what part of that half will be ours. It may vary between all and none. Beyond our immediate descendants, we cannot tell what is to become of us; we cannot count on even a minimum of permanence.

The paternal and maternal chromosomes do not combine in the child: they merely take places side by side. The two parental inheritances remain juxtaposed and unmixed in us. We are merely the site of an embrace between two heredities.

Our inherited substance, which makes us ourselves, is composed of thousands of small elements fortuitously matched and more or less fortunately grouped. We are a bric-a-brac construct. If a single one of the elements in the egg from which we came had been in the slightest particular different from what it was, or had merely changed position, the man born from it would have been another. What is this "I," Pascal would have asked, whose identity depends upon the nature or position of an atom!

Nothing can be of more moment to us than the rigorous machinery that controls the distribution of the hereditary patrimony. Yet, as I observe with a certain astonishment, most of us beget our children without a moment's qualm over the material connection between them and us. To the biologist, fatherhood presents itself in quite another light than to the layman. It is a game of heads and tails played with the chromosomes of one's forebears; it is a time extension allowed to half one's being; it is the late gift to oneself of a half-twin. Perhaps I speak out of character professionally, but it seems to me that a clearer awareness of just what our child is in its relation to us might bring a more precise shading to our ways of loving him.

The notion of one's own obliteration is less repugnant when half one's chromosomes have been passed on to livelier flesh.

No sooner do we have a child than we feel laid aside. We have become a lateral excrescence of the germ plasma. Our place is no longer on the axis of the future.

Heredity is not resemblance but inheritance. Bearing within us the makings of better and worse men than ourselves, we transmit to our descendants that which will make them different from ourselves.

There may very well be persons in the world more akin to us in their substance than our own blood kin.

Emerson said that the door of gifts is shut upon us at the day of our birth. More precisely, the inexorable door had already slammed nine months before, when the egg closed on the fertilizing element. Well before birth the obscure mechanism of cellular reactions arranges for each creature the chromosomal equipment with which he must play out his whole role. If we knew how to read human chromosomes as we do musical scores, we should find that there exist not merely dark and fair eggs, but charming and nasty ones, intelligent and stupid ones, and possibly virtuous and wicked ones. The fundamental iniquity of human destinies! As Shakespeare said: ". . . nature cannot choose his origin." It is a dreadful fact that nature produces the good and the bad with perfect indifference. To one creature she grants nothing but the right to be a stupid man, to another nothing but freedom to be an ugly girl; on certain persons she showers the qualities that life rewards, and on others inflicts traits that invoke every possible punishment. Biological privilege matches social privilege in cruelty. And to say this is by no means to seek in nature's wrongs an excuse for human ones; it is merely a reminder that nature here gives us, as she often does, an example *not* to follow.

At the outset each of us was pregnant with a multitude of possible beings. If our potential personality was first determined from among many possibilities by the accident of the germinal meeting, the accident of circumstances will later pick out our true personality from another similar multitude.

As Le Dantec said, an individual is a history: indeed, the incomparable history of an incomparable egg. We are ourselves, in the first place, because of the particular germinal inheritance that happened to be ours, and, in the second, because of all the particular circumstances of our individual lives. We are doubly unique: in our chromosomal make-up and in our personal life experience.

One cannot know where one's luck lay, until after the event. A life as often fails through poor opportunity as through poor heredity: as much for want of a grain of luck as of a grain of chromosome.

The differentiating influence of environment is at least to a small extent qualified by the fact that the milieu in which we spend the first months of existence is exactly the same for all of us. However different are to be the conditions of our lives afterward, we are all denied privilege during the nine formative months—all treated alike, warmed alike, nourished alike. One womb is just as good as another. And in this we may note an equality in principle which is neither fictive nor political, but biological and real. There is no equality of lot for humans except before birth and after death: in the womb and in the tomb.

Whatever the importance of germinal "grace," we must be on guard against the kind of biological Jansenism that would tell us the creature was predetermined in the egg. Environment is powerfully operative in human development. That is why, in a society like ours, governed by such a great diversity of conditions, we cannot hope to make even a rough calculation of the intrinsic value of individuals. How many well-conceived creatures have had the misfortune to be ill-born! One man is different from another at birth, certainly; but as long as each is not treated like every other, we shall be wrong to attribute patent inequalities to inequalities of origin. Let us beware of drawing conclusions about the egg from what we perceive in the adult.

Men will never sufficiently realize the contingency of their persons, nor to how slight a matter they owe it that they are not precisely what they despise.

If the egg does not contain chromosomes of high quality, no outside force will ever make a superior individual of its product. But the most benign heredity, on the other hand, can be squelched if it meets a too unfavorable environment. The individual is sometimes condemned by his chromosomes; he is not always saved by them.

The naturalist Weismann wondered what would have become of Mozart had he been born in the Samoa Islands. Many a Mozart is born daily on savage islands in our own so-called civilized society!

When one man talks down to another, there is seldom any reason for supposing that the best-qualified chromosomes are on the side of the insolence.

Biology points out the individuality of every being, and at the same time reminds us of the brotherhood of all.

For the biologist there are no classes—only individuals.

When man has succeeded in lessening (if not suppressing) the adventitious inequalities of rank and fortune, he will find himself faced with the terrible problem of natural inequality. What does the social group owe those aristocrats of the flesh, the better conceived, who have not had to lift a finger to acquire their promising chromosomes?

Are we to second nature's inequity by giving preference to those she has already only too well favored? Or ought we to practice the reverse injustice, by treating as equals those whom nature has endowed unequally? If we fail to reward the superior, shall we not discourage them from putting their excellence at the service of the collective interest? And, on the other hand, how cruel society would have to be to base its hierarchy on germinal merit, and thus deprive the inferior of the small compensation of challenging his sorry lot!

II

What we ascribe to heredity, said the philosopher Ribot, we take away from freedom. But that is not really the way the problem presents itself. The acquired is no less determined than the innate; thus the share ascribed to hereditary determinism reduces only that of circumstantial determinism.

Whatever an individual is—good or bad—has no causes other than the molecular make-up he received from his parents, and the external influences that have worked on him. Our thanks or blame must fall to chemistry and luck.

A given egg develops in a given milieu—and there you have the individual complete. One would hesitate to dwell on such biological obviousness, if one did not occasionally hear it said of some criminal or other that he lacks the excuse either of vicious heredity or bad upbringing. An odd statement, to say the least, worthy of Molière's M. Jourdain when he would have neither verse nor prose.

We tend to excuse a guilty man if we come to the conclusion that his brain cells were infected by some virus. But suppose, instead, they were vitiated by a bad gene? If we want to keep up our moral severities, by all means let's hold fast to the crudity of our knowledge.

Society has the right to protect itself against antisocial protoplasms; but it had better realize that when it thinks it is punishing a man, it is only chastising an egg or a set of circumstances.

The man who denies biological determinism probably does not know that certain actions are as clearly denied to certain men as are brown hair or a flat nose, when the appropriate germinal conditions are not present. Does he imagine his actions can change while he remains organically the same? Those who wish to preserve the notion of individual responsibility would, I think, have to believe that one is responsible for one's chromosomes.

That man who offends you—either he was born of a race different from yours or else he is your strayed brother: doesn't he, in either case, deserve your compassion?

What vast pity we ought to feel for those toward whom we are forced to act pitilessly!

To condemn the guilty is a necessity. But it is odious, since the culprit himself was predetermined. There is no human solution in a region where the *given* is inhuman.

We are the more pitiless with moral "monsters" the less remote they seem from us ourselves. Our harshness declines as we move along the scale from the human to the inhuman.

Perhaps our desire to punish a man stems not so much from his crime as from the discomfort he causes us by not differing from us except in his misdeed.

There is no creature so odious that he doesn't deserve to be pitied for his enforced membership in existence: miserable packet of sensitive jelly, tossed upon a hostile earth and obliged to cope with all the inward and outward business of it—with love, hate, fear, desire, other men, society, morality, ideas, the universe, death. Mitigating circumstance in all that a man may be: he is.

Feeling lays vain claim to the privilege of freedom for man. If animals are nothing but machines, man too must be one. When modern science confirms Descartes, it confirms La Mettrie. We are no more in control of our actions, glorious or shameful, than Pavlov's dog is master of his salivation when he hears the whistle that causes the salivary reflex. And isn't it precisely the conflict of the Cornelian hero—"immobilized," with "crushed soul"—that we see reproduced in the crouching and yelping animal, unable to respond at all, when it is appealed to by two antagonistic reflexes?

Even the man who believes in his freedom can have no illusion about its role with respect to the social or biologic factors of his conduct. As with a breeze blowing on a falling stone, the direction in which this freedom blows remains imperceptible.

If any such thing as "merit" does exist, we cannot evaluate it, because we cannot know what helps or hindrances the human will may have encountered: the man we call hero may actually deserve our blame for not having reached a higher point of virtue, while our villain may be rather deserving for not having plunged deeper into crime.

The choice of the germ cells and the preparation of the somata—these are the whole province of morality.

Our duty is this: to expedite the future. The first anthropoid that stood upright served morality better than the most affectionate of the four-handed creatures.

Science had better not free the minds of men too much, before it has tamed their instincts.

Can the individual who has reached a high degree of fulfillment because of a propitious environment expect to have superior offspring by comparison with the one who, given unfavorable circumstances, has always fallen short of his capacities? The biologist's answer is a categorical negative. The germ cells are not in the least interested in the individual's life experience; they keep no record of it— and thus, the race has no stake in it. We transmit nothing but what we have received from our parents, adding nothing of our own to the heritage. All we have acquired in our persons vanishes at our death. What is most our own of our "self" is the most perishable part. Our sons are less our sons than the inheritors of our line. Let us cease hoping they will owe something to our own experience. All we can do for them is to choose their mothers well.

Our germ cells have been formed in us long before we have become able to acquire anything whatsoever—before we have even begun to take shape. We procreate, so to speak, before we are.

An individual's deeds are of no use except to himself, or —through their results—to the community. We progress either for ourselves, alone, or for all.

Those successive accretions that make up the progress of civilization in the technical order as well as in the spiritual —do they not ultimately affect the very substance of man? Does not some part of the acquired become innate? Is social heredity never transformed into organic heredity? Certainly no one has ever maintained that such transmissions occur in any very precise way, or that the "young" of man, even after millennia of civilization, come into the world equipped with infused knowledge and morality; yet there are some persons who hold that by dint of learning and understanding, men have increased their aptitude for both, and that by fearing and respecting the rules of society they have become readier to obey them. Thus, although the content of civilization would not be written into the heritage of the species, it would seem that civilization itself, by its modification of habits and instincts, did operate to make the human stuff somehow more educable, more pliant, more open to the civilizing process.

If there is any truth in this—if in reality the social milieu created by man resonates in the human animal, affecting the very depths of that animal's substance—if custom, however slightly, becomes nature—then every hope with regard to the spiritual evolution of our species is permissible. From one century to the next, man would be born better adapted to society, his natural qualities would improve from generation to generation, and he would progress indefinitely in the very direction required by the collective needs. But science refuses us any such hope. The biological is totally ignorant of the cultural. Nothing of all that man has learned, felt, experienced through the centuries has been deposited in his organism—nothing of it all has entered into his flesh. No part of the human past has got into man's marrow. All he has added to himself has remained external and superficial. From age to age he has not become organically spiritualized. And if the whole of civilization were to be destroyed tomorrow, and man had to begin it all again, his starting point would be the same as one or two hundred thousand years ago. All his work, all his labor, all his suffering would count for nothing—would not advance him by an inch.

In this lies the great difference between the human and animal civilizations. Young ants, if isolated from the home ant-colony, at once reproduce it to perfection. But young humans separated from their kind would be unable to rebuild the human colony save in its lowest foundations. Ant civilization is inscribed in the reflexes themselves as a product of the ant chromosomes. Human civilization does not reside in man; it is found in his libraries, his museums, and his codes.

To suppose ourselves able to better human heredity by bettering the social environment is almost as naïve as to think one could cause Negro parents to produce a white child by painting them white.

Civilization is an expression of human chromosomes, but it makes no impression upon them.

We must not count on the fear or the hypocrisy of an ancestor to beget the virtue of his descendant.

Men of the twentieth century, however clothed, policed, and subtle, are substantially, chromosomally, identical with the stonecutters of the Pleistocene Age. Living anachronisms, their flesh is contemporary with that of the mammoth and the woolly rhinoceros. They can, to be sure, mold themselves to the complex demands of modern society, since it was men of their sort who set it up; but they are no more inclined toward justice, intelligence, peace, or altruism than their cave-dwelling forebears. "The human species," wrote Bonald, "is reborn with each generation." The infant man who at this moment is on the point of opening his eyes on the civilized world is precisely what he would have been had he been born a hundred thousand years ago from a similar grouping of chromosomes. No stage has been skipped for him. In some twenty years he will be expected to have covered the course that took millennia. The child of two individuals, not of two "social entities," he comes from as far off as the first thinking men. His mother rocks a belated Cro-Magnon in her cradle.

The man-child being born today belongs to no time, is unmarked by his epoch. Unshaped to society, he is also free of the deformities conferred by an imperfect society. The groundwork of his being is intact, he transcends duration, he belongs to eternal humanity. Although he does not come into the world superior to those who were born yesterday, he is in no way inferior to those who will be born tomorrow. If he perpetuates Cro-Magnon man, he anticipates future civilizations. He bears within him the mysterious and respectable matter of a citizen of the entire future.

If indeed it is from his ancestors that man is reborn in each generation, it is futile to look to time for a remodeling of the human stuff. Time does not work for man, and all one will have failed to do in this generation will have to be undertaken again in the next. I do not know what we can do with the human instincts, but I do know that whatever is possible can be done at once. The children to be born thousands of years from now will be no more suited to progress than those born now, and there is nothing for us to hope from the future which we may not already hope from our own present.

The newborn, springing up on the tree of the human species, strikes into our tired old world like a fresh, untrammeled bud. Exempt from all parental influence, free of all pasts, empty of all civilization, he has no solidarity with any part of what has been. Neither perfected nor impaired, he is as ignorant of our achievements as of our blunders. Man, and no more. Uncontemporaneous, intact, innocent . . . Let us respect this rebeginning, this renewal. Let us guard, as we inform, against deforming, against burdening this baggageless traveler as we provide for him.

Since our substance is that (or virtually that) bequeathed us by ancestral man, we must once and for all give up any prejudices with respect to antiquity of family, class, or people. No necessary laps to the course. All the possibilities of our protoplasm are fully present at the outset. An individual has nothing behind him but his own past. Between the crude state of the egg and the refined conditions of civilization there will never be any span but a lifetime.

The fact that the flesh of the species does not mature yields an argument for the social usefulness of the aged. Humanity, since it remains eternally young, has all the more need of its old men.

Will man, without progressing further, be able to go on indefinitely satisfying the requirements of civilization? If the gap between what he is at birth and what he is asked to become goes on increasing, will he not grow weary of having more and more to repress the beast in order to counterfeit the angel? Won't he then eventually rebel against demands that are too lofty for him, and ideals that are too austere? Without doubt the capacities of the human chromosomes have a limit. But nothing yet compels us to think this limit has been reached. One can have confidence in a genetic equipment that has managed to pass, in a few dozen millennia, from the cave age to the age of laboratories.

Since the first appearance of the human species, the surface of the earth has many times changed its face. Our hereditary patrimony is more stable than a continent.

"In the savage state all species are beautiful, because it is the strongest of the males who puts the others to·flight and possesses the female." Thus did Rivarol, before Darwin, express the idea of natural selection.

Clearly in many respects the purifying action of natural selection is contradicted in the human species by the progress of civilization. Female hips tend to become slenderer because the development of obstetrics has made it possible for the woman whose pelvis is too narrow to bring children into the world. And so with everything. There is no need of a Dr. Knock: the medical profession cares for its own future merely by cultivating the ill-adapted.

Biology surprises us somewhat when it teaches that, statistically, the most beautiful women are not the most stupid.

If is of the very essence of human civilization increasingly to oppose the merciless play of natural selection; and this it does as much through the powers of science as in the name of fraternity. Medicine will go on preserving more and more faltering lives; mankind will go on prizing, defending, guaranteeing human life, however mediocre in quality. A human fact no less natural than that of selection is in operation here. But precisely because man cannot and does not wish to deviate from his elected path, had he not better be wary of the danger to which his singular attitude exposes him? And in time to forestall the revenge of inhuman nature? This is the view of the eugenists, who hope to substitute for the old, crude, automatic selection a new, artificial, voluntary selection applied to germ cells rather than bodies. The less daring of these innovators would be satisfied to forbid the congenitally unfit to reproduce themselves, thus forestalling a new generation of congenitally unfit. The others would act more drastically: they would entrust the renewal of the species to none but individuals of exceptional physical or intellectual endowments. In their view such a course would, in a few centuries, raise the level of humanity to a point where the poorest specimens of the future would be the equals of the rarest geniuses of the present. Do we not betray our descendants if we pass up such genetic betterment? Humanity has a right to the best possible genes. To refuse them may be to prevent the birth of the man who is to vanquish cancer, free atomic energy, discover the secret of a more benign social organization. To refuse is wantonly to prolong suffering and disorder. And do we dare? Biology offers us the means of ennobling this refractory human nature which neither politics nor morality can change—this human nature whose imperfections balk the realization of every great, generous dream—this human nature which we hear invoked (justly, alas!) every time someone wants to discourage idealism. Can we reject this offer?

All biologists will, I think, agree that if humanity wants genetic progress it must use stringent positive selection. But the question remains: is humanity obliged to want such progress at that price? Will it ever consent to use its most precious representatives as breeders? And will even the hope of begetting a race of supermen make us think it admissible to employ ourselves as we do our livestock?

Here the biologist will refrain from taking sides. In a debate that brings into play so many different values, and in which the vital interests of the species appear to collide with certain needs of civilization, he will hesitate to raise his voice. Possibly this is because he fears his own boldness. He knows he would be inclined by professional bias to deal ruthlessly with the susceptibilities of the general conscience—and he is led to wonder whether his association with frogs and flies has left him human enough still to have any right to an opinion on the affairs of men.

It will be the task of future humanity to find an acceptable compromise between a too brutal "biologism" and an ideology too negligent of the goals of the species.

The idea of employing eugenic controls with respect to hereditary infections seems more widely accepted than that of using them to eliminate constitutional defects. We will challenge a man's right to transmit a microbe, but not that of transmitting himself. As though we cared more for the essence than the accident of a being.

Biologic morality? The man who absorbs too much alcohol will be punished by a cirrhosis of the liver. But not, however, unless his chromosomes have furnished him with an appropriate liver. Otherwise—no retribution.

Beginning now, man would have the power to act profoundly upon man. With no more than application of his present knowledge he could in a few generations raise both the physical and intellectual levels of his species. This progress, which is within hand's reach, he now rejects rather than owe it to a means which he considers incompatible with his dignity. But will he still refuse it tomorrow? Will he always refuse it? And won't mankind, pillaged by its physicians, eventually be forced to ask its biologists to restore to it in quality what it will have lost in quantity?

Man has the right, and possibly the duty, not to want to treat himself like cattle, but he should take note that what he is rejecting is the only possible means of increasing the biological distance between himself and the beast.

If a mature biology were ever to bring about the birth of a superhuman being, how would man react to him? Would he congratulate himself on at last having got a companion in his solitude, and on being able to expect from an abler brain the solution of those great enigmas which have baffled him until now? Or would he regret having made with his own hands the creature to whom he must now stand as an inferior brother?

All hopes are permissible to man—even that of disappearing.

Certain famous words to the contrary, I for my part refuse to think that man is a sufficient future for man.

A superman? We shall, perhaps, one day create that which will understand us.

III

Biology has reached the point where the results of its discoveries are about to impinge on man himself. We have had to applaud the conquests that have made this young science into a sort of practical magic, but how can we look on without being a little troubled as it extends its empire and prepares to try its powers out on the hitherto untouchable human person? In their laboratories scientists are now playing with insects, frogs, fowl. One reverses the sex of a chicken by introducing a certain chemical into the embryo. Another, by pricking an egg with a needle full of blood, brings a fatherless tadpole to birth. A third changes the eye color of a fly with a tiny drop of lymph. . . . And in future shall we be able to avoid turning these strange recipes to our own account? Tomorrow our own children will be used as experimental material. Their sex will be predetermined, their physical and moral personalities will be designed by dosages of supplementary hormones. In this respect, at least, let us not envy the future too much. For my own part, I prefer to have lived in the barbarian age when parents had to be satisfied with the gifts of chance, for I doubt that these rectified and calculated children will evoke the same emotions as do our present variety, fortuitous, imperfect, and disappointing as they are.

The day we are able to fashion human beings, what will be left of our old prejudices concerning merit and blame? What will be the reactions of men who have every right to say: "I was not born as I was supposed to be; I am not I?"

One can foresee that science will soon achieve command over human conduct and will confer a sort of artificial virtue on individuals. But for those who believe in the soul, it goes without saying that that entity would not be in the least affected by such technical means. Evil souls would simply find themselves compelled to good behavior. They would, however, be no less reprehensible, and hell would then be paved with good deeds.

It is not true, as certain biologists have supposed, that there is a difference of kind, a difference of value, between the germinal cell and the body cell. Each of the quadrillions of cells of which we are composed contains us, potentially, since each is equipped with our forty-eight chromosomes and thus harbors the whole of our inheritance. We are repeated millions of times within ourselves. We remain all that we are, down to the very least of our elements, which thus participate in our uniqueness.

We have learned from tissue cultures that most of the cells composing the organism have a limitless power of multiplication. In each of us there is an immeasurable reserve of life: there is stuff to furnish the beginnings of worlds of protoplasm. Today one could, then, challenge the total death of any creature, by cultivating cells taken from his body. And so long as the irreproducible combination of chromosomes to which he owed his individuality were to remain present in any morsel of life, one could not consider him absolutely annihilated—for nothing forbids that science someday learn how to rebuild a complete being from the starting point of a single one of his cells:

The majority of the elements of which we are made are potentially immortal. Death is a collective phenomenon.

To how many animals is human biology not indebted! The horse ascarid and the vinegar fly have taught us about the mechanism of heredity; a bedbug has given us the secret of sex; the bat has taught us about fertilization and about the first few hours of embryonic life, as has the rabbit about certain later stages. We required a whole menagerie to teach us about ourselves.

It would no longer be possible, of course, for a Buffon to heap crushing scorn on those who work with flies—or necessary for a Réaumur to defend himself against the charge of sacrificing life to petty and futile amusements. But do even those who look with condescending sympathy on the work being performed with small animals understand the extent of our debt to these creatures? Do they sufficiently realize that our deepest knowledge of ourselves has been acquired from them, and that it is from them we can expect our future revelations? The present science of man has not been built upon man, or even on the larger animals, but on tiny flies of the sort everyone is familiar with and pays no attention to, and of which hundreds can be raised on a slice of rotten banana in a small bottle.

The layman is willing to admit that sea urchins, and even frogs, can be brought to fatherless birth by artificial procedures: the fact does not even especially astonish him. But he refuses to believe that the method could ever become applicable to "real" animals—that the livestock breeder might one day produce calves without a bull, or colts without a stallion. The biologist makes no such differentiations. Chemical impregnation of rabbits has already given him multiple-celled embryos; between these invisible rabbits and the larger, fleshed ones of reality the distance is slight, he knows, and may be spanned any day now by a simple technical advance. Possibly the day is not far distant when we may be able to cause human birth without a father. What sort of creatures should we expect to result? Everything points to the probability that they would be females, and precisely like their mothers—a sort of younger twins.

What novel emotions would the mother not feel toward such remarkable offspring—in whom she would survive totally? These integral daughters in whom she would see her own youth repeated, while they, on their part, could study their maturity in her? Would she relish seeing herself too faithfully reproduced? Would she be jealous of these new versions of herself who would have the future to themselves? And they, would they not feel some resentment at being mere replicas of her?

Perhaps there would be a strong temptation to bring about one's own rebirth in this way; but, on the other hand, might one not feel considerable scruple against inflicting one's being on another? In our ignorance we have no hesitation about creating life—but would one dare, wittingly, to create a *particular* life?

The knowledge of hormones has given us indiscreet precisions. We know today the exact molecular make-up of certain of the substances that condition the differentiation of sex. We can represent them by a few letters and numbers; we prepare them by synthetic processes; we obtain them in the shape of handsome white polyhedrons. It would be using rather unscientific language, yet not at all incorrect, to say that femininity and masculinity can be crystallized. Taine would surely have been delighted with this reduction of them to simple chemical species, much like the sugar and vitriol that he took to represent virtue and vice.

The most vaporous of women owes her sheerest femininity to a certain complex alcohol or sterol which can, among its other capacities, change the plumage of the capon and swell the uterus of the mouse. As for man, he is forced to admit that he gets his proud virility from another sterol (incidentally, only very slightly different from the first) which also acts to darken the sparrow's beak and the thumbs of the frog. And these two principles—estrogen and testosterone, so powerfully and diversely morphogenic—are not restricted to working upon the body: they affect the instincts, the tendencies, the desires; entering into the nervous system, they color mind and soul; they have as much to say about the play of fantasy as about skin contacts. So, wherever testosterone predominates, a strong attraction will be felt for the forms modeled by estrogen.

Whether one likes or not, and whatever the idealism one may subscribe to, the whole edifice of human love—with all the word implies of animality and sublimation, of rage and sacrifice; with all that is frivolous, touching, or terrible in its meaning—is constructed upon the minimal molecular differences among a few derivatives of phenanthrene. Is this a de-poeticization of love? Or might it be a poeticization of chemistry?

Only a slight differentiation of structure separates the chemical compounds that compose the male and the female. Nature has divided the species inexpensively.

The determining principles of embryonic organization are found in the liver, kidney, heart, and brain, as well as in the egg. Similarly the fertilizing elements are found not only in the male cells, but in the globules of the blood.

Accordingly, there are some who would say that one finds almost anything almost anywhere in the living organism. But, joking aside, we must admit that the revelations of biochemistry leave little ground for the old conception of the body as a workshop with each substance in its proper place, as though shelved by a farsighted and meticulous chemist. Nature is nothing like a well-ordered pharmacy.

By subjecting the vinegar fly to X rays we get him to produce all sorts of abnormal offspring which, in turn, can give rise to new races. Thus we make monsters banal and prodigies commonplace. "By art likewise we make them [animals] greater and smaller than their kind is. . . . Also we make them differ in color, shape, activity, many ways." So speaks a member of the imaginary Institute of Salomon in Bacon's *New Atlantis*. Likewise, the twentieth-century demiurge, Müller, can say: "I have succeeded by the techniques at my disposal in producing dwarf flies, short-winged flies, and white-eyed flies." Because the subject is "only" a fly the public hasn't yet realized the importance of this success. Up to now the genetic material of the higher animals has seemed resistant to the effect of radiation. But doubtless more powerful mutation techniques will soon be discovered. And it is now possible to imagine a day when man will employ who knows what agent of change upon his own chromosomes, his old chromosomes, which have not altered since the Cro-Magnon age, and within which supermen may be slumbering.

"Man's dream," wrote Maeterlinck, "is to be a passer-by who will not pass away." But really man would be satisfied merely to be a passer-by who would pass away a little less rapidly. To be sure, the progress of medicine, surgery, and hygiene has notably lengthened his life. But it is not enough for man that statistics allow him a better-founded hope of reaching old age and completing the life span nature assigned him. His dream is to outlast his time and live more than his allotted years. He does not dare, however, to think this anything more than a dream. And even when he hears the possibilities of rejuvenation seriously discussed by scientists, he mocks his own hopes. He thinks it reasonable that science may fortify him more and more against the accidental causes of decline, and may increase everyone's chance of running his race to the end; but that science should propose to push back the limits set by nature, act upon the natural span, make death wait—this seems to him utterly chimerical; and a challenge to the inflexible needs of the species strikes him as insane, almost monstrous audacity.

Actually man cannot believe in such a victory because it would be too precious. And there is anthropocentrism in his disbelief—for to doubt that our desires can be accomplished is to pay them great honor. There is really every reason to admit that aging is a physiological process like any other, and accordingly susceptible to being altered by experimental methods. Today the biologist acts upon all stages of the vital cycle. Sometimes he slows or stops a process, sometimes he accelerates or stimulates. He is in command of growth and of cellular differentiation. He shifts the rhythm and succession of the major bodily events. He creates dwarfs and giants at will; he produces monsters *seriatim*; he brings on the puberty of a mouse, the laying of a hen, the metamorphosis of a frog. He creates new races and species. He manipulates heredity, he reverses sex. No act of life seems beyond his reach. Why, then, should senility be an exception? And why, since senility is a fact, should we stand by and look on at it indefinitely? If in the end it were to resist the biologist's efforts (as the process of radioactive changes balks the physician) this would be a real singularity, and science would have to account for it.

Old age makes its debut in the germ plasm, and goes on developing until death.

The younger the subject, the livelier the process of aging. The person who ages least rapidly is the old man.

Man is distinguished from most other mammals not only by the length of his development but by the length of his whole life. His heart can manage four billion beats as compared to the million generally allotted his class neighbors. Nature is in no hurry to part with human beings; she allows them to see their successors grow up and mature. She permits them to make use of what they have gained during their long youth. It is only by lasting out his time that man can exploit his destiny—can become what he is. Furthermore, the results of age are not without advantages. An old man is not merely one who, by dint of time, has carried his own development far: he is also a satisfied man —his ardor is cooled, he is freed. Something would be at fault in humanity if the individual continued on in life without growing old, and if death gave no warning before it struck.

In prehistoric times the rigorous competition for life kept man from reaching extreme old age. It is to science and social progress that he owes his opportunity to make the utmost use of his capacities; one has a rather good measure of the degree of a community's civilization in its statistics of life expectancy. If it is true that prolonged childhood is responsible for a good part of human ascendance, one might say schematically that the child has made civilization and civilization has made the old man.

The inculcation of the social feelings is made possible only by the state of dependence and fear in which man spends the whole of his childhood. He would not develop into a virtuous animal were he "born adult," like the guinea pig.

Education equips us with ephemeral knowledge and tenacious dislikes.

If, as Lecomte de Noüy holds, aging hastens the flight of the hours, if time loses value in proportion to its shrinkage along the path ahead, then human life is far shorter than we tend to think: evaluated in "children's years" it would probably not have a total span of more than twenty. Man would then seem, in spite of appearances, to resemble those insects that spend the greater part of their lives in the larval stage. Whence it should follow that we ought to show a somewhat greater regard for the period of childhood, and refrain from continually tormenting children for the good of the future adult.

No reciprocity possible between two beings separated by a large number of years: we live more briefly with our sons than they with us.

Age astounds more than it oppresses me.

Our brain cells do not renew themselves as do those of the skin or the blood. We are condemned to harbor all our lives the very elements our misfortunes have scarred.

IV

When we think of the beginning of the organized world, we are obliged to imagine certain infinitely simple structures capable of giving birth, by a series of transformations, to the whole fauna of the present. The mind boggles less in acknowledging the genesis of a speck of protoplasm than that of a man; and when it comes to evolving man from this speck of protoplasm, we feel free—since we have thousands of years in which to bring it about—to bury the mystery in sheer extent of time.

So—on the earth's crust there once took shape something extremely lowly and of negligible appearance which had the singular capacities of assimilation and growth: or, in other words, of converting external matter into self-matter, of vitalizing the inert. Did life arise at one point only, or at several? Did it spread from one spot to another like a spark? Was it like a sudden conflagration? Was it from the beginning diversified? Whatever the case, a day came when cells were born of the initial protoplasm. Then these cells formed groups. Then—to speak of the animal line only—differentiation and organization resulted in, first, the invertebrates, and next the vertebrates, starting with aquatic animals and proceeding to the walkers. Earth and sea were full of paradoxical forms. In this youth of nature (for Pascal's celebrated tag applies to more than human nature, and the ancient organisms must be called "young" in contrast to the "old" forms of today) there existed all those primitive animals whose remains are so startling to eyes accustomed to the "old" well-classified nature. To think of them in all their confused multiplicity is to be reminded of children's paintings—great with promise and containing in germ everything the artist is to unfold later on. There were creatures, neither fish nor fowl, that bore traits both of the ganoid and of the salamander; there were ambiguous things, part reptile and part mammal; disparates that were both reptile and bird. Little by little, the groups as we know them now established themselves. Lungs separated from fins, wings from teeth, shells from mammae. For a very long period of time brute matter went on exerting its crushing force, not upon "thinking reeds," but on barely sentient ones. At length, after several thousands of centuries, in a particular family of placental mammals, occurred the series of transformations that were to lead to the upright monkey with sky-pointing forehead, in whom the universe would seek a meaning. . . . Perhaps we shall never know in detail the steps of the evolutionary venture. But from the philosophic viewpoint this does not matter. What does matter is the point of departure and the point of arrival —the speck of protoplasm and the man. At the final stage of the inorganic, the assimilating ooze; at the final stage of organization, the reflective animal, the thoughtful beast, gifted for speculation, susceptible of torment, capable of remorse.

For a very long time after our planet had broken away from the sun in the shape of an incandescent drop, it remained desolate. The high temperature, the intensity of radiation, precluded life. Life was capable of infesting only a cooled and aging earth—like the proud flesh known as *thrush* which sometimes forms in the mouth of a dying person.

What was the source of the first germs of life? To say they came from another planet is to defer the problem, pointlessly; the only rational conjecture is that they took shape on the spot from a combination of chemical elements whose properties were still capable of such impressive syntheses.

Without for the moment having any idea what conditions governed such a genesis, we have no reason to think they are bound to remain unknown forever. If truly life issued from inert matter—if it is not a primitive *donnée*, but the result of a particular arrangement of molecules, it is perfectly possible that man may one day reconstruct the causes of the phenomenon—may with his own hands light the torch that generations, throughout the ages, have been able only to pass on to one another—may imitate nature in the creation in which even she cannot imitate herself. At such a moment contemporary nature and man together would match pristine nature.

Supposing man were to become capable of creating that unknown to which he owes being, he would doubtless produce a protoplasm unlike any that now exists. And in that case, why not the principle of a new tree of species? An entirely new series of living creatures, called into existence this time by man, would then refertilize the earth and compete with the old natural life of anonymous make.

Many biologists think we now hold the key to evolution: that it came about by means of those sudden alterations, or mutations, which are constantly taking place in the hereditary substance of living beings. Accordingly, those variations we note in our laboratory cultures would illustrate in abbreviated form the phenomenon by which we were begotten. Nature would be pursuing her development before our eyes. Furthermore, we should be in a position to hasten evolution; we could compel life to progress faster than it chooses—for we can already cause insects to produce a profusion of aberrant forms by submitting them to a bombardment of electrons. For my part, I still doubt that mutation represents the true evolutionary change; it is my feeling that variations of another sort must formerly have taken place—ampler and more constructive variations, of which nature no longer offers us examples. Does this seem a lazy solution? But even the most ardent actualists are forced to admit that life no longer arises on this earth, where once it must have arisen. Life must have made its appearance and evolved, must have risen from the inanimate and lifted itself to the level of consciousness, always by virtue of the same powers of synthesis, which today are in abeyance. Inorganic matter was once capable of becoming animate, but rapidly lost this capacity. For some length of time, young life was able to innovate, but little by little the evolutionary faculties receded. Today life has everywhere run its course. It is no longer constructive; no longer evolving. We belong to an old, deadlocked, stabilized universe whose innovating faculties are dried up. Having once and for all fashioned its living models, it can no longer do more than repeat them in endless copies.

Let us note that the inorganic world, no less than the organic, is on the downward path. We are witnessing nothing but phenomena of disintegration in it. We observe the formation of light atoms at the expense of heavy ones, and never the reverse. We see the ruin of atomic structure, never its rebuilding.

Organic evolution is very far from presenting a general landscape of superlative harmony and majestic pertinence wherein all is for the best in the best of all possible natures. As old Theophrastus observed, there are many ill-made things in the living realm. We know of animals that are barely able to eat and to reproduce themselves; of others as malformed as it is possible to be without ceasing to exist; and still others whose useless and hidden eyes seem to favor the Lucretian hypothesis that organs were not made for use, but use created by the organs. If we pause in our beatific praise of nature and make bold to cross-question her, we find out that she is generous in errors and superfluities, in gratuitous or harmful complications. And how often have we not—like the naïve interpreter of Pascal, Victor Cousin, who took a misprint for a stroke of genius —praised nature's cleverness for some organic pattern

47

which later proved to be either useless or else actually injurious!

Doubtless there are also many successes in nature; but philosophically these make less sense than the failures. Blind necessity might be able to counterfeit design, but design would not be capable of counterfeiting blind necessity.

Listen to certain biologists and it will appear that nothing in the realm of living nature is harder to understand than the origin of minor organic details such as the calluses on the knees of camels, or the snap-fastener ornaments on the crab's shell. I, for my part, am more embarrassed by the camel as a whole—or even by the crab.

Our way of judging the works of nature must be rather like that of the layman judging a work of art. Full of absurd astonishments. If there is anything to be amazed at in nature, it is surely not where we think.

If God were manifest in the structure of creatures, biologists would have too great an advantage over the common run of men.

It has long been acknowledged that living creatures in their childhood stages generally resemble the adult forms of their ancestors. This was expressed in the classic formula: the individual recapitulates in its development the entire history of the species. But we do not lack numerous instances in which, on the contrary, it is the adult form of the descendant that resembles the youth of the ancestor. The juvenile form is not necessarily a reminiscence; it may be a promise for the future. One might find analogous facts in the mental sphere. Doesn't the superman, the genius, retain certain intellectual or emotional traits of childhood? "Every child is to some extent a genius," said Schopenhauer. And Baudelaire: "Genius is merely childhood clearly formulated, and endowed at last with manly and powerful organs through which to express itself."

Nothing is more relative for the biologist than the notion of the monstrous. All living things are monsters to one another. Man is a monster by comparison with the ancestral primate. The amoeba is a monster by comparison with matter, which itself is monstrous in the view of the void.

What we can perceive of the struggle for existence gives only a feeble idea of the universal massacre. At every instant, germ cells, either within wombs or out, are perishing, embryos being aborted. The deadliest natural hecatombs occur without bloodshed or strewing of corpses. To be born is, itself, either an extraordinary piece of luck or an extraordinary misfortune.

Granted that changes which occur in the individual do not affect his descendants, we are obliged to conclude that

49

organic evolution came about by germinal alterations. It is in the germ cell that all reforms and all enterprises began. Far from being a simple echo of the organism that harbors it, the germ cell itself is the first speaker. Thus the grandiose phenomenon of evolution was in some sense a confidential affair, realized at the level of the invisible world. The first human was not born in the open but in the microscopic enclosure of a cell.

Whatever the causes responsible for the appearance of man, they are in any case the same that brought to light all the rest of living nature. The problem of our own origin raises no special difficulty; the moment we learn how the leech or the fly came to be, we shall thereby and thereupon know how the wretched lord of the planet was first born.

Biology denies man any essential attribute that does not belong also to all other living creatures. Whether he likes it or not, he trails them all after him like an immense army of the poor with whom he is obliged to share all he arrogates to himself.

Whether Pithecanthropus was a man or a pre-man, whether or not he possessed fire and could dress stone, is in itself of no great importance. Is he our direct ancestor? On the subject of filiation all is conjectural; but what matters to the philosopher is to know whether any intermediaries existed between the beast and us. Pithecanthropus was one such being. Certainly the transformist hypothesis, which definitively re-established man in the animal world, needed no supplementary proofs; but we are more aware of the disturbing reality of this hypothesis when we consider the narrow brainpans of those creatures in whom simian traits begin to be tempered in the direction of the human.

If these near-men had survived until now—if, instead of having to picture them on the basis of a few vestigial remains, we saw them living side by side with us—what a blow to the esteem we cultivate for our species! Would we continue, under their equivocal eyes, to boast of our privileged essence? Would we dare repudiate these undesirable relatives, and immolate them—as we do the other beasts—to the needs of our science?

The extinction of Pithecanthropus, by sparing our pride, has exonerated us from certain scruples.

Man has partly digested his "zoologic humiliation," just as he has the cosmologic variety. He is growing used to the idea of being descended from a beast, as to the idea that the earth is not the center of the world. But he balks at owning his descent to the monkey—the great monkey that he knows so well: he prefers not to have the image of his origin before his eyes, and would rather be related to some remnants of bones than to a creature of flesh.

Certain minds, while they admit the reality of organic evolution, see the human species as a long-premeditated masterpiece. Although he bulks so small, man represents in their eyes something quite other than a simple accident or episode of becoming: the "thinking reed" is not only nobler than "that which slays it"—it is the *raison d'être* and the goal thereof. Even as Mallarmé said that the universe was created to lead to a great book, so they hold that the universe in its totality has existed in order that, at a certain hour, in a certain spot, the fragile human being might make his appearance. But there are other minds that see things in an entirely different light. These, with all the best will in the world, cannot manage to discern in nature any concern whatsoever with man; they think that life has evolved as best it could, without care, without protection, without any mysterious connivance on the part of the rest of the universe; they think that man was neither prepared for nor expected—that in order to maintain himself, he had to struggle hard against a hostile environment; they think that nothing foresaw and nothing willed the heavy and anfractuous brain of *Homo sapiens,* and that if the small mammals of the Tertiary period had not had a taste for the eggs of the great Sauria, the animal kingdom would have had a different lord; they think that human thought, intrusion that it is, has no more importance in the inert cosmos than the song of the tree frog, or the sound of wind in the trees; they think that intelligence has conquered the earth only by severe struggle and because intelligence gives strength, and that if a more powerful or better-adapted species than ours were to arise tomorrow, the domination of the planet would fall to it by right; they think that man is only who he is, that he embodies no thought but his own, that his value is exclusively self-referent, in accordance with what he thinks himself and makes himself, that he possesses no rights but those he arrogates to himself, no duties but those he imposes on himself, and no mission that is not self-assigned. . . .

It appears that in the Tertiary age organic evolution was still active enough so that human observers, had they been present, might have witnessed the transformations of life. Thus we missed only by a little the opportunity of seeing nature move. What a curious coincidence that she should have stood still just when she was on the point of providing herself with a witness!

When Nietzsche wrote that the goodness of monkeys made him doubt man could be descended from them, he was mistaken about the qualities of those greedy, cruel, lascivious four-footed creatures. They are in fact the *perfect* ancestors for us.

Man, the psychologists teach us, owes a good part of his dominance to the power of imitation, so much more prominent in him than in his animal forebear: he is man only because he is more "monkey" than the monkey.

There is nothing to prove that nature's realities, and especially the more profound of them, are translatable into our human dialect. It is clear that prehistoric men would have been incapable of resolving the intellectual problems that we can resolve today. Why should one assume that *Homo sapiens* has now reached precisely the level of intellectual capacity that would enable him to understand everything?

Man may flatter himself with being the best thing they turn out in the workshops of the unknown.

If biological evolution had been "directed" by the animals, it would never have led to man.

The supreme deed of nature was the creation of antinature.

It is widely thought that if our species were exempt from both sickness and the ills engendered by social imperfections, it would thereupon be purged of all flaws. A gross illusion: nature knows how to impair herself, for there is nothing static about her, and her changes are more often deteriorative than improving. It is apparently the same sort of phenomena that built man up in the past which are at present breaking him down.

Whether man is disposed to yield to nature or to oppose her, he cannot do without a correct understanding of her language.

The attempt to derive everything in man's history from some single factor—technique, the need for knowledge, etc.

—would seem to be an error. There is no "organizer" of human embryogenesis.

Planetary systems, although hardly commonplace by comparison with the vast numbers of the stars, must nonetheless teem in space, where the galaxies abound. Among the multitudes of distant planets which we have reason to suppose exist, are there any peopled by a life comparable to our own? Each of us is free to speculate on this in his own way, favoring the frequency or the rarity—even the uniqueness—of the human accident. But according to what we know of the exceptional properties of protoplasm, its genesis would require a highly improbable confluence of circumstances. Furthermore, it is most unlikely that any other given mass of protoplasm would undergo the same series of transformations as resulted, on earth, in ourselves. I can see nothing at all to prevent our world from monopolizing the tragic privilege of the human brain, and from being the only spot in the universe where the blind play of molecules ends in speculation and suffering.

Thus life seems likely to be a rare occurrence beyond the confines of earth; as for humanity, there is every probability that we terrestrial men are its only representatives; and in this species, which without doubt has not its like elsewhere, each individual is, himself, matchless. Every one of us is a certainly unique object in a probably unique group.

V

What are we? What is our position in nature? What is the sense of our existence, the value of our activity? Keeping strictly to the terrain of science, here are the answers, more or less, one might propose for these questions.

Like all the higher animals, man is an aggregate of several trillions of cells, each representing an assemblage of diverse molecules. On final consideration, he seems to be a prodigiously complex structure of electrons, which owe the singular privilege of being able to affirm their own existence to the particular way in which they are grouped. As for thought, man's chief pride, the cells of the cerebral cortex are the governing elements of organic architecture. In this membrane occur those chemical reactions and transformations of energy which produce consciousness—a phenomenon about which we know nothing, except that it is inseparably linked to those reactions and transformations. It is in the cerebral cortex that the supreme manifestations of the mind take shape: the genius of a Newton, the anguish of a Pascal. . . .

If the brain cells are deprived of oxygen for a few minutes, consciousness is blacked out. If the privation continues for a quarter of an hour, the irreversible changes induced by cellular asphyxia result in the permanent disappearance of consciousness. Never again in the world will that particular consciousness make itself felt; nothing more will be heard from that "I"—unique as every other "I"—and dependent upon the intactness of those particular cells.

A lightning flash in the night—so thought has been described. One might better call it a glow, vacillating and always under threat of extinction. Indeed, it would even seem that the only capacity thought possesses is that of observing the action of the machine it has the illusion of commanding. The so-called act of will appears reducible to a pattern of co-ordinate reflexes, and man in his moments of reflection, deliberation, and calculation no less under compulsion than the caterpillar creeping toward the light, or the dog responding with a flow of saliva to the experimenter's whistle. The grave moral decisions to which man attaches so high a value would seem, then, to be mere effects of social stimulation; and when he thinks he is conforming to the sacred imperatives which he thinks he has himself selected, he is no more than an automaton aroused in conformance with the interests of his group.

Where does man come from?

From a deviant line of animals, now extinct, which includes certain jellyfish, crawling worms, viscous fish, hairy mammals. . . . By this chain of ancestors, whose lowliness increases the further we move backward in time, he is attached without break of continuity to the microscopic elements that were born from the earth's crust more than a billion years ago.

An accident among accidents, he is the outcome of a series of chance events, of which the first and most improbable was the spontaneous formation of those peculiar carbon compounds that came together in protoplasm.

Man is far from being the creation of a lucid will; he is not even the culmination of a blurred and confused effort. The blind and disordered processes that conceived him were not seeking anything, not hoping for anything, not tending toward anything, even in the vaguest way. He was born without reason or goal, as were all creatures, no matter how or when or where. Nature has no favorites, and man, in spite of all his genius, has no more value for her than any of the millions of other species brought forth by terrestrial life. If the stem of the primate family had been cut at its base by some geological accident, reflective consciousness would never have appeared on earth. It is, moreover, possible that certain organic families which were destroyed during the course of the centuries, would, had they survived, have given birth to more accomplished forms than ours.

In any case, man did appear. . . . From a certain animal life that gave no hint of such a destiny, there sprang forth one day the absurd beast that was to invent integral calculus and to muse on justice. A pessimist might well deplore the arrival of this paradoxical creature, weighed down by his superiority, and owing only an excess of suffering to the hypertrophy of his intelligence and his affections—this creature who goes through life in fear of death, who attaches himself too strongly to other ephemeral creatures, who—being either too animal or too little so—suffers when he represses his instincts and no less when he yields to them, who cannot defend his heart against the dreams his reason forbids. . . .

It is true that humanity has persisted for hundreds of centuries, in spite of conflicts and agonies. Statistically, at least, men prefer being to nonbeing. And that is sufficient cause for the triumph of optimism—which is content with very little.

But let us leave to the moralist the job of weighing individual suffering against satisfaction, and inquire what man as member of the species may be permitted to think of himself and his labors.

Certainly if he recalls his origin he has good reason to regard himself with complacency. This grandchild of fishes, this great-nephew of snails has a right to some parvenu pride. Who knows how far he may go in his mastery of the forces of matter? What secret will nature succeed in keeping from him? Tomorrow he will free atomic energy, he will travel in interplanetary space, he will extend the span of his own life, he will fight most of the ills that assail him —even, by improving his social organization, those ills his own passions create.

His success is enough to turn his head. But he can sober himself instantly merely by giving his ridiculous kingdom its place among the innumerable stars his telescope reveals. For how could he go on taking himself seriously from any point of view once he had looked on the icy reaches where the spiral nebulae are speeding?

What outcome can he predict for his works, his effort? What part of it all will survive on the wretched grain of mud where he dwells? The human species will pass as the dinosaurs and the Stegocephalia passed. Little by little the small star that serves as our sun will lose its power to give light and heat. . . . Then, of the whole civilization, human or superhuman—its discoveries, philosophies, ideals, religions—nothing will persist. There will be less vestige of us than we today possess of Neanderthal man, whose few remains have at least found refuge in the museums of his successor. In this tiny corner of the universe the odd adventure of protoplasm will be finished forever. . . . This adventure which may already have come to its conclusion in other worlds . . . this adventure which may be about to begin in still others . . . And everywhere sustained by the same illusions, provocative of the same torments, everywhere just as absurd, as vain, as doomed from the outstart to ultimate failure and to infinite darkness . . .

Will this ephemeral creature, dwarfed in the immeasurable cosmos, at least be allowed to think of himself as repository of a privileged value capable of defying the norms of duration and extension? I cannot see upon what he could found the notion of any such value. It is useless for him to soothe himself with the hope that what he is participating in exceeds his own measure. His labor does not enter into any sort of absolute. He must be content with his own domain, irremediably shut in, having no communication with vaster worlds. The only duty that devolves on him is to improve the human realm and to assert his sway more and more over insensible nature. If he takes himself to be the instrument of some nameless purpose, if he flatters himself that he is serving ends which transcend him, he does so in vain. He is preparing nothing, he is prolonging nothing, he is linked with nothing. He is not conniving, as Renan imagined, in an "eternal policy." All that he holds dear, all that he believes in, all that matters in his eyes, began in him and will end with him. He is alone—foreign to all else. There is nowhere any slightest echo to his spiritual needs. And all that the surrounding world offers him is the spectacle of a somber and sterile charnel house where the triumph of brute force is staged in disdain for suffering, indifference toward the individual, the group, the species, and toward life itself. . . .

Such, it seems, is science's message. It is arid. Up to now, one must admit, science has done no more than to give man a clearer consciousness of the tragic strangeness of his condition, while awakening him, as it were, to the nightmare that grips him. One has some ground for hoping that she will in future learn to use her power to give man moral ease and emotional peace. It is possible, for example, that progress in cerebral physiology, or simply in psychoanalysis, could bring about such a modification of our psychic responses that we might come to accept without anguish the discords which are inherent in our condition.

Science has gone too far to stop in her tracks; what we must now expect is that she will add to her blunt teaching such means as might prepare the human mind to receive it. It won't suffice for her to instruct us of our nothingness; it is essential that she make us capable of tolerating it. It won't suffice that she remove our illusion of having a task of infinite consequence; she must take away our need of it. It won't suffice that she deprive us of our feeling of freedom; she must regulate the operation of our machine in such a way that we come to accept ourselves as machines.

It could happen that an all-powerful science succeed definitively in creating this new man, adapted to the human condition, satisfied to be no more than what he is, fulfilled in his narrow destiny, cured of all the dreams that outdistance him. But it could also be the case that humanity as a whole prove incapable of bearing the truth of science.

An arduous truth—crushing, oppressive . . . Among her zealous followers themselves, there are some who cannot submit to it without distress. To be sure, they cannot do otherwise than remain loyal, but they do occasionally envy those who are not prevented by the form of their own minds from conceiving of a different form.

In procreating man, that child of her old age, nature gave the last sign of her fertility. If only she had become sterile a little sooner! Her disorders were still benign, her slaughters innocent, while the animal who knows he must die had not yet made his appearance.

Man is a miracle of no interest.

It is possible that even the loftiest of minds cannot comprehend the universe; but the least of those who suffer in heart has the right to incriminate it.

In making man, the universe presented itself at one stroke with a victim and a judge.

Science has no more to teach us on all the points that matter to us. Either she already knows everything or she will never know anything.

The reign of science has opened a sort of glacial era in the mental history of our species: we have as yet no clear proof that the shivering human soul is able to stand the rigorous climate of reason.

It could be, after all, that the development of the human intelligence constitutes a case of harmful orthogenesis —like the antler development among certain deer.

If man is to bear life, the help of all truths and all illusions would not be too much.

Man, that poor monkey condemned to play man . . .

Belief in a thing can't be founded on the reason that life would be too horrible if it did not exist! Proof by means of the horrible is no proof.

The fact that nothing is intelligible does not give us any right to surmise the absurd.

Metaphysical uneasiness flares up in proportion to one's effort to subdue it: it is like those persistent itches that are made worse by scratching.

However vast the field of possibles, it is not yet big enough to offer man the little he would have been content with.

There are fewer things in heaven and earth than are dreamt of in our philosophies.

The human brain: monstrous tumor of the universe, in which questions and agonies proliferate without curb, like malign cells.

My contradictions do not disturb me much: far from being a philosopher, I am a worried biologist.

My heart, like most others, desires the survival of the whole man; my mind, however, longs to escape from incomprehension.

I cannot get along either with those who shun the blunt truth or those who make their peace with it too easily.

I approve of man's suffocating in reason, but holding fast to it.

Some men, although they entertain no illusions about the foundations of things, spend much skill in embellishing the surface with verbal graces. The void knows no flourishes. And since nothing these men have to say can prevail, let them leave us in peace to savor the abiding tartness of despair.

The whole dignity of man lies in daring to look in the face a truth that is unworthy of him.

The only thing that might make me a little suspicious of my dark convictions is their excess.

Those who are most submissive to the rigors of reason may have most need to be free of them.

Man, when all is said and done, has nothing to say about man. Since there is no one else to pass judgment on him, he may magnify or shrink himself at will—like a madman, who, without risk of contradiction, could choose between delusions of grandeur and of inferiority.

66

The only boast man can lay claim to: that nothing more complicated than he is to be found among molecular groupings.

The ant has no idea it is nothing but an ant; but man knows he is only man.

Man has every right to like and admire himself to his fill. But let him beware of rationalizing his narcissism and trying to give meaning to the series of incidents which, by adding a pound to the weight of his brain, has given him lordship over living things.

The part of man that refuses to be merely an animal is yet itself animal.

Once thought is not all, it is merely an aberration of nonthought.

Man is suffocated in man.

I do not know what man is made of, and care very little what the substance is called; but what I think I do know is that it is a poor stuff and one that gets worn out in the span of a life.

I cannot manage to believe that when we are dead we are any less dead than when asleep.

Metaphysical nausea brings on a hiccuping of why's.

The inert, not the living, has the upper hand in the universe. To die is to join the stronger side.

Kill a man, one is a murderer; kill a million, a conqueror; kill them all, a God.

To affirm immortality is to blaspheme against the frailty of the person.

Man has no recourse but to forget the brute immensity that ignores and crushes him—to work at becoming as "uncosmic" as the universe is inhuman.

Human consciousness has given the universe a bad conscience. It won't recover its pristine peace and innocence until the day it will have wiped out the pitiable success of certain cell-agglomerations that took it upon themselves to begin thinking.

A proposition I never question is this: that forces alien to our hearts have made playthings of them.

Claude Bernard when he was dying said: "It is not suffering I protest, but suffering for nothing." So might humanity say.

Nothing counts—not even all the somber courage of which we might make show in nothing's presence.

The deeper man's thought, the more he is sucked down into the human.

Intelligence adapts man to his immediate environment by giving him the means of resolving his lesser problems; but by allowing him to confront the great ones, it disadapts him to the universe.

All is tragically simple for the individual human: nothing to understand, nothing to expect, and there would not even be anything to suffer from, were man able to do otherwise.

We shall never know everything about anything, said Pascal. But the worst of it is to know that even everything about everything would leave us unsatisfied.

There are no valid answers for the one who himself poses the questions.

For us, there is nothing to understand; and apart from us there is no one who *could* understand.

We are so constructed that we cannot be satisfied with the truths we have access to. "You would not seek me if you could find me. . . ."

The terrible thing about dying is to vanish without having understood. The crime of death is not in killing us, but in conferring eternity on our anguish by cutting it off.

One of man's worst miseries is to be unable to blame his suffering on anything, and to have no recourse when it becomes unbearable but to take it out on other victims.

Starry heaven and moral law: double subject of amazement for Kant. What actually is rather surprising is that respect for the latter can endure under contemplation of the former.

Since we are no longer able to be a mere animal, wouldn't it be better not to know that we are one, at all?

It cannot have been worthwhile for man to comprehend his nothingness if he was, nevertheless, to keep all the ills he got from his greatness.

Man's mind leads him into sufferings that are far above his station.

All man gains by getting to know his worth is to lose even his respect for his suffering.

The great human mistake is suffering. Woe unto the woeful! And the universe triumphs in the heart of a happy scoundrel.

It is not his genius that astonishes me in this descendant of the brutes; it is his gift for suffering.

How can one still take part in the human turmoil once one has grasped its insignificance! Even a game must be taken seriously if one is to find any amusement in it.

This solemn philosopher knows perfectly well that life is a pitiable farce; but this fool has no doubt that he is witnessing a magnificent adventure.

71

The truth, it seems to me, has a taste for revenge; I refuse to do reality the favor of deluding myself about it.

I cheapen the world like those who keep adding to it, but I do not add.

VI

The human brain, like a teacher's handbook, contains in advance all the problems and all the answers, too.

Contrive not to take one's miseries as problems, unless there are no others.

Man is as incapable of giving up his noble actions as of finding a satisfactory meaning for them.

Man will never live according to his despair, but no more will he ever come to hope according to his life.

Those fine secular trees whose shade seems so necessary to the human soul—will you remember that they have no roots but cling to the surface of the soil? Like toy trees. It is up to you not to shake them. . . .

How can we manage to take those things really seriously whose seriousness depends entirely upon ourselves?

Willy-nilly, we live on what we deny.

Might our hopes be nothing more than the pretexts for our impulses?

When life seems tolerable, we do not ask it to have meaning; it is the heart's upsets that make the mind too demanding.

Said X.: "I don't go so far as to demand a god; all I ask is that man not prove to be merely a scrap of unusually complex mud, that mind not be a meaningless exploit of matter, that there exist a sort of vague something toward which one could turn at those times when one's distress is too great. Isn't there anything at all between horror and fairy tale?

It was nature's innocent misdeed to compose living beings out of the substance of things.

Belief in personal immortality might be described as a dislocation of the "body image"—but in time, rather than in space: allotting oneself extra duration the way certain invalids provide themselves with an imaginary limb.

Man is soluble in nature.

The only thing of which I am really sure is that we are made of the same stuff as the other animals; and if we possess an immortal soul, then so must the Infusoria that inhabit the recta of frogs.

I will always refuse to think that a dead man and a dead Pithecanthropus are separated by the difference between a cadaver and a piece of carrion.

Believers resent my materialism, and the others resent its lack of jubilance. . . .

I know perfectly well that unreserved negation gives one the appearance of being a simplicist, summary, coarse mind. I know that in this realm of ideas there is everything to be gained by leaving all doors open, and by taking refuge in the infinite complexity of phenomena, and by deferring to the unpredictable possibilities of the unknown, and by alleging the bottomless ignorance of man, if not, indeed, the essential infirmity of his mind. Yes, I know . . .

It is possible that materialism is wrong in affirming nothingness; but one must admit it has good reasons for the darkness of its outlook.

Nothing is more touching than the desperate effort of so many minds to find, cost what it may, a meaning for human existence. Participation in the infinite, collaboration with the absolute . . . These are the pitiful formulas of thinkers who, without themselves having any strong belief, try to rescue a little of man's noble paraphernalia.

Almost all the demonstrations of the philosophers would tend to persuade us that, although evidently there is nothing there, yet somehow, all in all, it's really quite the same for us as though something *were* there.

The ballast that human hope is compelled continuously to throw overboard . . .

Certainly we can act as though we had a soul. . . .

We purify God, we simplify Him, we pick Him bare, we accept His silence and His idleness. We accept the fact that everything goes on down here as though He did not exist. We ask Him merely to keep His name.

It is man's fate to create more and more believable gods in whom he will believe less and less.

Will man really be able to tolerate having become such that he can no longer think himself such as he would like to be?

Renan said: "I should sell my country for a philosophic truth." Of course; and much else, too.

All that our minds have dreamed is baffled in our flesh.

The contortions of poor humanity when it is weaned from the impossible . . .

It may appear, statistically, that humanity will not give up its illusions except as it gains strength to do without them; but what is true of the group is not necessarily so of the individual. Some minds are unequipped to secrete the amount of illusion they would need.

I should hesitate to deprive any being of the illusion he lives by; but humanity as a whole interests me only insofar as it can stand up to truth.

The words of philosophy are no less apt to lose their punch than those of slang.

Rare indeed are those who live without secret hope. The merest touch of mental laziness is enough to feed an unacknowledged doubt.

Beyond despair there may be something which is not altogether resignation.

The greatest homage paid the unknown occurs when the materialist, by chance, happens to doubt nothingness.

I am anyhow not witless enough to be altogether sure of my certainties.

Nothing is too little; God would be too much.

Those who would need a God most are neither the worst nor the best.

When I consider the majority of believers, I am astonished that they, who differ from me so much in thought, should differ so little in deed.

Those who believe in a God—do they think about Him as passionately as we, who do not believe in Him, think about His absence?

If I were to believe in a God's silence, it would be that of a God who had never spoken.

Believers sell their bodies to God.

God-trickery: an immortal making himself beloved by means of a pseudo-mortal.

Complement to Pascal's wager: what if it could cost us our immortality to have subscribed to rubbish?

In the course of normal human development, the instincts, which have at first been entirely fixed on self, detach themselves partially, in favor of other persons. But what happens for the individual cannot occur for humanity. Dissuaded by reason from seeking a love object other than in herself, humanity can only resign herself to narcissism.

Man is not a "dispossessed king" but a parvenu who possesses enough to make him afraid of his own power.

The naturalist Barbellion, in his *Journal of a Disappointed Man*, laments: "As lonely as a god, without being a god." Intending to speak of himself alone, he described the whole condition of man.

Human solitude: our pride has the same source as our anguish.

79

In man, nature flourishes and disowns herself. In man, that denatured monkey . . .

Make a God, or else remake man.

It may not have been altogether necessary that man know himself to be an animal before becoming a highly social animal.

It is asking a great deal of man to demand that he at once despair and obey.

Man—a disconcerting beast that does not even need a master to hold him in check . . .

Man's nobility is his belief in it.

In the presence of the universe, man exhibits all the demandingness of an only child.

Will man someday grow weary of vainly cursing his absurdity and of vainly seeking a meaning for himself?

How frightening the human intelligence that allows us to look down upon ourselves, and thus sometimes leads us to think as though we were not men. To disdain the human is to assume the role of a god.

To make use of the fact that one can think, in order to cast aspersions on thought, is going a little too far.

To suffer from our humanity is to bend under the weight of the air that surrounds us.

Few people are worthy of not believing in anything.

The inanity of all moral epithets for our species. No name suits the name giver.

There is something in man that transcends even the transcendent.

The infinite and closed world of thought . . .

I do not believe in mystery; it would be too simple.

From childhood we cling to that strange need that things be higher than ourselves. The child wants to be a man, and the man to be . . .

To be adult is to be alone.

To succeed in giving life some weight without making it too heavy, that is the whole problem.

Life, a game of massacre. The same philosophy cannot serve both the man who has already been knocked down and the one who is still on his feet.

It would be better—said a celebrated philosopher—to be an unsatisfied Socrates than to be a satisfied hog. Undoubtedly. But isn't a Socrates—even a satisfied one—more to be pitied than a hog—even a discontented one?

The contentment of certain individuals makes one think of that "mindless euphoria caused by any extended lesion of the frontal convolutions" (J. Lhermitte).

One must either take interest in the human situation or else parade before the void.

No one is more convinced than I of the vanity of all things, or less skilled in putting this certainty to use.

In spite of its inept treasures, the world is bereft of what I would need. How many things there are in it that cannot satisfy me!

Staying on to the end of the show does not take away one's right to criticize.

This life that one cannot take seriously, and which one must sometimes take tragically . . .

I still understand a few words in life, but I no longer think they make a sentence.

I do not believe in the harmfulness of pessimism: distress is not catching for others, and it may well come to the aid of another distress.

VII

In proportion as science increases her power, science feels less assured of her knowledge. Like a person afflicted with a "failure neurosis," science finds occasion for her gravest doubts in her greatest triumphs.

Science has made gods of us before we have deserved even to be men.

A few great minds are enough to endow humanity with monstrous power, but a few great hearts are not enough to make us worthy of using it.

Just a short time ago the "geoclastic" phantasm of Dr. Obnubile* crossed the threshold of the possible. Planets, we now know that you are mortal. . . . And how could

* In Anatole France's *Penguin Island.*

85

we fail to be terrified when we realize that such gigantic means are now in the hands of such a disunited species, incapable of putting the good of the whole before its clan interests or tribal preferences?

The invention of the atomic bomb must at least have made us see what research can do when it is called upon. The problems of cancer and tuberculosis would take no longer to resolve if a country felt the necessity of resolving them. What stands in the way is that they are important for humanity as a whole.

For years man dreamed of freeing the energy stored in the atom. Hardly has he realized his dream than he begins to groan at its danger: were we then so naïve as to think we were going to play with harmless toys right to the end?

Since the discovery of atomic disintegration, it has become incumbent on humanity to live under threat of death. Why shouldn't the feeling of lethal danger, which is so productive for the individual, be so for the species, as well?

Science: the only way of serving men without becoming a party to their passions.

The misdeeds of scientism? Maybe. But what about those of "philosophism?"

I'd like to ask those who maintain that science doesn't explain anything to explain once for all what they mean by explanation.

There is nothing consoling to be deduced from the uncertainties of science.

Dream, probability, certitude: three stages of scientific truth. But, like those bodies that pass directly from the gaseous to the solid state, the dream sometimes "sublimates" itself in certainty without even having crossed the phase of probability.

It is always injudicious for a belief to build its nest in a dark corner of science.

What relief from oneself there is in science!

I do not think research workers have much to fear from check-ups and arrests. No one is clever enough to foresee just where the inopportune truth may arise.

Truth is discussed coldly, but created hot.

It is sometimes important for science to know how to forget the things she is surest of.

Science must shake the yoke of all philosophies, including the one of which she is leader.

It is a piece of luck for a scientist not to notice those facts that would get in the way of his being right.

Truth is always served by great minds, even if they fight it.

When a scientist is ahead of his times, it is often through misunderstanding of current, rather than intuition of future truth. In science there is never any error so gross that it won't one day, from some perspective, appear prophetic.

It is after truth has been discovered that we become aware of the simpler approach by which we might have reached it.

Woman like, truth is not always difficult in proportion to its beauty.

It is sometimes well for a blatant error to draw attention to overmodest truths.

There are big and little truths, but all belong to the same race.

Nothing leads the scientist so astray as a premature truth.

Falsity cannot keep an idea from being beautiful; there are certain errors of such ingenuity that one could regret their not ranking among the achievements of the human mind.

One must credit an hypothesis with all that has had to be discovered in order to demolish it.

If a given scientist had not made a given discovery, someone else would have done so a little later. Johann Mendel dies unknown after having discovered the laws of heredity: thirty-five years later, three men rediscover them. But the book that is not written will never be written. The premature death of a great scientist delays humanity; that of a great writer deprives it.

One cannot bring a given set of truths to light without obscuring others. Every discovery covers up.

The enemies of science are agreed in using her audacities as well as her prudences against her.

Those who have no hesitation in making utterly naïve judgments are equally bold in invoking the scientific spirit, to deny science the right not to deny anything.

The only thing one cannot embellish without causing its death is truth.

Science, that creation of man, is assuredly uncertain, relative, subjective, fragmentary, provisory. But what has antiscience to gain by saying so?

I do not know what the value of science is, but I am quite sure that those who imagine they increase the prestige of human illusions by depreciating it are much deceived.

It does not take science to put the mind into a state of distress: reason is quite enough.

Science's uncertainties are no less relative than her certainties.

Scientific truth does not generally reach the majority of men until it has ceased to be true.

The true delight of the scientist is to sniff from a distance the matchless odor of truth in its nascent state.

Nowhere does the mind better demonstrate its power than where it excludes itself in order to try to understand itself.

It may be the selfsame faculties that the human mind uses to penetrate to reality—and to distort it.

One must be careful not to take for a precursor the man who contradicted yesterday's truth merely because he hadn't caught up with it.

In conflicts of systems, as in wars of nations, the victor almost always finds himself somewhat altered by the vanquished.

The secrets which would have greatest importance for us are not always the best guarded ones: improving the functioning of the human brain might be no more difficult than altering the ribbing of a butterfly's wing.

It is by means of scales that we detect weightlessness.

There are certain hypotheses which behave like what are known as "dead" grafts: no part of their substance lasts, but they have tutored new ideas.

One can generally gauge the progress of a scientific question by the simultaneous simplification of its major lines and complication of its small details.

It is not exceptional in the history of the sciences for a thinker to be honored for something that he would certainly not have thought at all had he thought more exactly.

Truth, perched on her pedestal of errors . . .

Idea and technique are no less inseparable in science than substance and form in art.

If Alexander Jordan had not been a Catholic he probably would not have discovered the constancy of the "little species." If Jacob Loeb had not been a pure materialist he would doubtless not have invented artificial parthenogenesis. . . . If scientific truth is not "of all systems," as

Claude Bernard said, it is at least diverse enough to owe something to all of them.

I am amazed that it is considered permissible to whittle away at genius, and that there are people who dare to decide that a given great man would have been still greater had he thought differently. Do we then know so well the sources of their superiority? Those whom I myself revere I take whole, just as they are, and—materialist as I am—I would not wish Pasteur not to have had religious belief or Mendel not to have been a priest.

Even if the time came when no problem could hold out against science, what solution could hold out against the interrogating mania of the human mind?

The daily fresh supply of solidly based ignorances.

Leave all doors open—but bar entry fiercely.

It is not talking nonsense that offends, but talking it in the name of principles.

What opinion is not open to question in our day? This man is abnormal, says the psychoanalyst. But the psychoanalyst is steeped in bourgeois ideas, says the Marxist. But the Marxist is a believer, says the rationalist. But the rationalist, in turn . . .

I think I would tolerate my opponent's dishonesty if only it had the honesty to recognize itself for what it is.

Every research worker, doubtless, has his blinkers. Pray at least not all have the same.

The peril that hangs over all dogmas is that of creating suns that can be stopped.

One would be tempted to say to certain scientific workers who are overconfident in their teaching: possibly, indeed, you have laid hold of the truth, but for heaven's sake, forget it somewhat while you are searching for true particulars.

It is always a windfall for truth when well-established facts collide with a well-constructed theory.

One has no right to be right except with the facts at one's command.

If the future should not resolve the problem at hand, it will certainly make us see its insolubility in a different way.

Truth always holds in reserve something with which those who were on the wrong side may have a bit of revenge.

Take a fact that present notions do not permit us to explain. Were we to wait twenty years, there would be no difficulty at all in explaining it, had it not in the meantime been found to have been false.

Only the historian of science knows how many valid objections truth has to survive before winning acknowledgment.

Science is larger than all systems, and nature larger than all science.

I would not want even Truth for dictator, since it could come to pass that she fail to recognize her true servants.

Cybernetics: man is more skilled in imitating thought than in imitating life.

It is well for truth to undress only a little at a time: she dare not spare us a single one of her veils.

What a theoretician must never forget is that, were he to be right a thousand times in succession, the facts are holding in store for him a thousand chances to be wrong.

We must not suppress the incomprehensible, but neither must we use it as an explanation.

It occurs to me to wonder whether two errors battling each other are not more fruitful than a single truth reigning without challenge.

If one thing is sure for me, it is that doctrinal plurality is favorable to the search for truth. "Vitamins" and "oligo-elements" are as indispensable to the health and fertility of the mind as to those of the body, and from everything that tends to thin out the intellectual realm we may well fear the unpleasant effects of malnutrition.

However remote the adversary may be from our corner of truth, he may yet be closer than we to a truth we have no inkling of.

How could a man be sure enough of being right to want to be faced with nothing but silence?

How few things there are of which we are so sure that we would want them to exterminate their opposites!

Truth dead at birth—like all that lives.

I cannot believe in anything except what we are going to believe tomorrow.

I should resent wanting to be more persuasive than truth.

Even if one thinks one knows the basis of things, it is well to be on guard against prejudging their surface.

The essential thing for a scientist is to have clear perception in his own domain; and who cares if Pasteur did not believe in evolution, or Lamarck *did* believe in spontaneous generation?

It is generally the feeblest part of a doctrine to which a man's name remains attached.

Here's somebody who quite rightly rejects radiesthesia, psychics, astrology; but if he means to reject psychoanalysis in the same breath, it only goes to show that nothing is rarer than discernment in negation.

We do not hesitate to rebuke the psychoanalyst for the monotony of the themes he attributes to the human unconscious. But do we equally rebuke the surgeon whose knife exposes entrails that strikingly resemble other entrails?

If there are persons who oppose psychic research because it would challenge the traditional notions of science, I must protest that I am not one. Far from dreading a disturbance of my mental habits, I long to meet the fact that would invite me to revise my philosophy of the universe. I would give the whole of science and her rich splendors for one of those little phenomena that the psychists record with such nonchalance. I would give my wholehearted applause to any evidence that might enlarge our concept of man and infuse something unexpected into the frigid cosmos of reason. If I yielded more to pleasure than to proof, this indeed is the direction I should take. Why in heaven's name, then, do I hold to my own sad assurance? Alas, I do not see it on the point of being threatened. . . .

Consoling truths need twice as much proving.

VIII

Times have changed since Pascal; soon the astonishing thing about a book will not be finding a man in it, but an author.

It would be all too easy to be a great writer if no more were needed than heart, cleverness, and impudence.

How many books there are that make one wish for a little more naïveté of soul and a little more finish of style!

That the natural may, by chance, give rise to art does not make it follow that art must produce naturalness.

It is always perilous in art to make use of freedoms others have won.

The part of an author most easily imitated is his soul.

Biology teaches us that almost all the innumerable variations which occur in human species are characterized by deficiencies. Similarly in art, most originality is subtractive.

Analysis deforms. In this it is art.

It sometimes happens that a mediocre artist's sketch resembles the completed work of a master; similarly the larval stage of one animal may resemble the adult of a more perfect animal.

To be able to observe with a stranger's eye helps one to see with an artist's eye. What alienates us inspires.

Even in the most tenuous work one not infrequently finds enough adventitiousness to obscure what is essential.

There are certain masterpieces of such fastidious workmanship that one wonders how anyone could be found to write them.

The danger of negligence is that it may allow something worse than itself to be seen.

It is fairly customary for the virtues of a work to be magnified by the presence of its defects.

This book—what's missing in it? Perhaps simply a little less perfection.

One would quickly grow weary of perfectly normal geniuses. A little neuroticism, if not indispensable to excellence, is certainly so to its refreshment.

The work of art: a method of eliminating certain internal poisons, like the silk cocoon for the Bombyx caterpillar.

What poverty there often is at the source of originality! The well-provided man does not go in quest of new worlds.

Few works of art can compel attention without some sort of commotion. Far better that this should occur around them than in them.

The unfortunate part of lacking secondary qualities is that one overesteems them in others.

One is sometimes reconciled with art by a work that is not an artist's.

How much restraint is needed in excess!

It is not modest to despair when one reads masterpieces.

Greatness, in order to gain recognition, must all too often consent to ape greatness.

I bow to the book that condemns me to read it.

Sometimes, by surprise, one admires oneself in someone else.

In true love, according to Nietzsche, the soul must envelop the body; so, in art, inspiration should envelop craft.

One can be surer of the talent in minor works than of the genius that seems present in major ones.

I do not like little things, but occasionally I find greatness where others see only littleness.

The case of literary merit is like that of human longevity: winnings are based on average rather than maximum achievement.

The great books are those that grow with man.

Quantity is sometimes the only resource of those who had nothing to say.

I am weary of all that is old, and I have no confidence in the new.

Beauty in art is often nothing but ugliness subdued.

One is almost always disappointed by the writers one admires, and surprised by those one scorns.

For a writer who tells all, I find that Z. says little.

X. has nothing of genius but its stupidity.

Men are certainly no less hideous than this writer paints them; but they are more subtly so.

There is more pleasure in thinking about than in re-reading certain writers.

X. is made of rawhide, but impenetrable.

A "beautiful" book is one which produces, while it is being read, the same impression of inanity that all literature gives when one is in a calm state of mind.

It is not good for a writer to play scientist, nor for a scientist to play writer; but the writer is not forbidden to know, nor the scientist to write.

Literary creation is nothing but a prolongation of ontogeny.

Literary giants, like other sorts, often have small heads.

In the realm of mind there are, among the enduring works, some that remain alive and full of sap, while others subsist only like splendid fossils, typifying an age.

Here and there an imperfect little work of art will outlive a big, imposing one, built in the manner of a masterpiece: so certain mouthless insects outlived the great Sauria.

The work of art may precede the environment to which it will be adapted; certain whales are born on dry land.

In art as in nature fertility often goes hand in hand with a high mortality among its products.

Certain writers' names, by conditioned reflex, cause admiration to be secreted in advance: once produced it has got to be used.

All literature has grown up on surface sensibility just as has organic life upon a thin layer of vegetable earth.

Just as most living organisms cannot build up their substance except at the expense of other organisms, so most artists make use of matter that has already been elaborated by someone else. There are, however, some who, like the autotrophic bacteria, are able to make direct use of the crude elements of reality.

Critics who find purpose in the smallest details of masterpieces make one think of those naturalists who assign a role to every least hair of living organisms.

Great inequalities in the terrain of the mind create the disequilibrium propitious to genius.

We know that, for reasons implicit in its principle, the microscope has reached the limit of its enlarging power. It is the same with psychological analysis in literature. In the one as in the other, future discoveries will require less direct methods.

The only thing certain writers could count on to make them popular would be a "mutation" that would raise the average quality of individual sensibility.

Genius has catalytic powers: it allows the realization in cold blood of certain spiritual acts which under ordinary circumstances require the high temperatures of passion.

Self-dissection is more easily accomplished than self-definition.

Difficulty discourages me; facility repels.

X. writes with his blood; but his blood is ink.

Like those animals whose blood maintains the same degree of heat in spite of external temperature variations, there are writers who know how to keep their pride constant under all changes of opinion about them.

In art as in morality there is much well set-up depravity.

Those who live most intransigently are those who have no means of expression.

Poetry is not always to be found in poets, nor truth among scientists.

Some writers are such frauds that they would ask us to believe green cheeses were made of the moon.

A masterpiece is an abscess of fixation.

Occasionally the reading of a writer's intimate journal makes me want to know his books. The animal having caught my interest, I am curious to see what he produces.

I like sentences that give the effect of being cut out from some invisible context.

I read a man's memoirs to learn what he has not been.

A whole book, sometimes even a whole life, may not be too much to authenticate a few lines.

In art as in life the valid sacrifices are those that bring no income.

There are some writers one hesitates to praise, so much would one seem to be pleading one's own cause.

The goals of art are no less murky than its means.

Certain works are to be reread periodically—for self-measurement.

For certain books, survival is due punishment.

A marvelous spectacle to behold in art: supreme skill disinterestedly employed.

The height of genius would perhaps not look like genius at all.

There is a certain insipidity even in X.'s most brutal confessions; he has perfumed guts.

When we envy someone else his "*savoir faire*" what we want it for is to keep ourselves from using it the way he does.

The man who puts too much of his life into his art often puts too much of his art into his life.

An artist must try, scrupulously, to render truth, but have the luck of not being able to do so.

What is sometimes missing in a writer who wants to reach the top is knowing how to start out low enough.

Doubtless X. would have talent if he warmed up; but isn't he too intelligent to do so?

The only advantage of facility would be to allow one to be harder on oneself.

It is only very great works of art that survive without having lived.

My own preference would be for a style in which the reader would feel neither the decision to write nor the stand against it. What I like in detached reflections is that they need not be the outgrowth of any style.

Style ought to continue shining even when turned off.

To create a work with the sap of life . . . But life dries up quickly when one spends it thinking about the creation of works.

I prefer a simple notebook to all books; but one must write books, as well, in order to keep the notebook from becoming one.

The writer uses his fire to make paper.

Real work lies in knowing how to wait.

One would like to think of darkness lying beyond all the clarities.

My book is finished today: will it be so tomorrow?

"This is all good material," you say; "something ought to be made of it." I, on the contrary, when I look at other people's work, sometimes regret that such fragile constructions should absorb such precious matter.

I enjoy discovering in a writer's notebook the unity of a mind and the disorder of a brain.

Too easy, you say, of fragmentary writings? No doubt; but, far from seeking the difficult, I try to make everything easy for myself so I may try for the one thing I can do: transcribe myself.

As soon as thoughts are ordered they begin to seem less sincere.

If one doesn't write for oneself, it is well at least to know whom one is addressing; let us avoid skew-eyed writing.

By means of work one exceeds one's capacities.

One isn't emptied by producing; the outside books attract the ones within.

There is time for writing, and time for becoming the man who will write.

Try to acquire each day an atom you would regret not having been able to make use of before you disappear.

Don't wait to believe in yourself until it is too late. . . .

I should have liked to be one of those writers who uses clipped phrases to discourage long developments.

It is a little too strong for my palate when a style has the air of knowing what one might say about it.

We haven't much to learn by keeping company with minds of our own kind. Better get our lesson from strangers, who take us away from home ground.

Shall I finally someday write a book that won't justify my own sneer?

Better write a book that reflects one wholly; others won't take the trouble to put one's pieces together.

Fear not: you will always have enough pain to inspire you. . . .

Writing: the only way of stirring others without being bothered by a face.

Try not to let phrases discourage words.

Always guard against weakening by addition. Respect the touching economy of truth.

Why this despair in rereading yourself? What did you imagine you had written?

Every now and then one needs to drink again from one's own fount.

Bizarre mania, this examining myself. I am far from interesting myself in proportion to my self-scrutiny.

The only thing in myself that interests me is what remains unpredictable.

We must expect chance to furnish us our thoughts.

If one does not present oneself honestly in talk—so be it! But with writing it is another matter. One is compelled to talk, not to write.

With no one but oneself for model, there are only too many portraits to be made.

I am usually poor at penetrating other people's characters; and even when I am concerned with feelings of which I have little experience, it is still to myself rather than to others that I turn for lessons.

When we write a sentence we cannot foresee the part of ourselves a later rereading will reveal in it.

I prefer the honest jargon of reality to the outright lies of books.

I could never fully trust a man who writes too well. One never knows what talent is made of.

Take heed of critics even when they are not fair; resist them even when they are.

Considering what they choose to quote from me, I really find them very indulgent. . . .

It is sometimes on one's weakest limbs that one must lean in order to keep going.

The books one has written in the past have two surprises in store: one couldn't write them again, and wouldn't want to.

I fear failure—but in my own view, not that of others.

I postpone endlessly the hour in which I shall agree to judge myself.

If we set a high value on certain obvious things it is because we have won them arduously.

The important thing for a writer is to be an expert on himself.

An aptitude for discovering certain merits goes hand in hand with an inability to respond to certain others.
Inequity is necessary in creative taste.

It is not unusual to seek to redeem oneself from one's works by one's criticism.

I know that Z. is a great writer, but I can't help feeling that those who don't admit his greatness have more sensitive taste than I.

What subtle taste one must have to discern so many merits in Y.—but what naïve judgment to think it matters!

Good taste can't get along without some asceticism.

We allow ourselves lapses of taste which we would deny to others.

At the very best we never have more than scraps of taste.

A writer does not necessarily have the same taste as consumer that he does as producer.

The only possible good judges are those who do not have to give proof of good taste to themselves or to others.

Would those who explain him, dead, have recognized his worth, alive?

Esthetic pleasure? I don't deny its existence, but I regret that there is no instrument for measuring it; one would see some odd discrepancies between the figures and the enthusiasms.

How can one judge a newborn work? And, once people have begun talking about it, isn't it already too late?

If a "connoisseur" had attempted to judge the living species at their outstart, he would certainly have been much mistaken about their respective chances of success.

Certain writers take advantage of all the bad taste there is in good taste.

Usually people fail to recognize the qualities of an author unless they stand out to the point of being faults.

We are as naïve with respect to writers as with respect to men: we believe in their advertised qualities.

It is a contradiction in admiration to bestow itself on certain works before withdrawing from certain others.

There are people so mistaken in their admiration that they praise a work for the very thing to which it hoped to be an antidote.

Our disdain often has better taste than our envy.

How could I fail to admire this book, transfigured as it is by universal esteem? All I can say is that if it had depended on me I doubt that it would have become what it is.

We are occasionally made aware of the value of a book we had taken for a failure, by its having caused us to judge the author with more than usual severity.

A writer of any cleverness at all finds it relatively easy these days to make himself virtually unjudgeable.

When a man's mind is too well armed, he can no longer feel admiration except when emotion disarms him.

What a failure this book has been! People have rushed to praise it, under the illusion they were praising something else.

A writer who doesn't contradict himself leaves his commentators too little to do.

The only things one can admire at length are those one admires without knowing why.

The secret of many artistic successes lies in having given a good conscience to bad taste.

The very tenuous line between what one has written and what one would not for anything in the world have chosen to write—who is capable of perceiving it?

Our taste is the product of certain delicacies and of having surmounted certain others.

A great writer is a man who knows how to surprise by telling us what we have always known.

The all too subtle intentions of some writers put me in mind of the delicate shell hues affected by certain small male crustaceans whose females have no eyes.

A writer takes no pleasure in being praised by those who are unaware of all he has not permitted himself to say.

To have better than human taste is perhaps not to have good taste.

As there is in art false greatness, so false littleness.

If one knew why one writes, one would by the same token know why one lives. Writing is a biological function in which all the instinctual factors of a being participate.

The work of an author who knows too well what literature should be makes me think of the handwriting of a man who knows graphology.

That the best of our fellows never, or almost never, prefer what is best in us is the hardest thing of all to accept.

Certain writers take on the bad taste of their age, like those fish that have a taste for mud.

The banalities of exceptional writers furnish good quotations.

Is it really worth working so hard over one's clarity for so many people with blurred eyesight?

To please the crowd is to please only one.

It takes courage for a writer to do justice to those who have the very faults he is charged with.

The stupidities of the masses cancel out, those of the elite add up.

Even the great dead are not safe from the stupidity of the living.

We must watch over our modesty in the presence of those who cannot understand its grounds.

Great modesty is disarmed only by great honors.

How tiresome are the modest! As though it were not enough to have to listen to the story of their success, one has had to pry it out of them.

A little success enslaves; much frees.

It isn't because grapes hang out of reach that boors don't like them.

Unjust scorn drives us to curry unworthy esteem.

I don't know which is more despicable—servility in response to honors, or servility in anticipation of them.

It is easier to hide altogether than to remain in sight and refrain from playing a part.

Compensation for writing? I could more easily understand being paid for abstaining.

Dream material: an immensely glorious reputation about which one would never hear anybody talk.

The purpose of the masses is to form the elastic medium over which the vibrations of a name may travel; the only good of glory is that it leads to the few.

How much useless noise a name must make in order to reach a heart . . .

There comes a certain acceleration of glory when those who were afraid to break silence begin to fear that they may go unheard in the general outcry.

Don't be astonished at their having attained glory, but judge the garment as they wear it. . . . If you are hungry for fame, there's no telling whom you may have to see served before you!

In the presence of avowed ambition, how can one help thinking of the well-known "grain of sand" on the point of lodging itself in the urethra. All ambition, for me, smells of death. My own is no exception.

The great man is the parasite of the crowd.

I should be no less greedy than the next man if I could forget that all that is, is nothing. . . .

Even better than a disdainful mind—a disdainful life.

I sometimes feel that I have had enough of having none of those things I have no wish for.

There is no one like an independent for doubting the independence of others.

One cannot help overrating the things one scorns. That fellow who refused the Legion of Honor is a vigilant scrutinizer of lapels.

Accept honors without scruple or else refuse them without regret: they are surely not worth a struggle of conscience.

Honors? Too late to get into the race. I haven't the required temperament or the training. And by comparison with all those men waiting in line, what royal serenity . . .

One turns away from the honors hunt when one knows oneself well enough to predict a mediocre bag.

The thing I hold against rebels is their secret passion for officialdom.

Honors evaluate a man for all those who are incapable of judging for themselves. And for the others, too.

Enviable, perhaps, are those whose ambition is directed to the attainable.

We allow ourselves to be impressed even by the honors we have with our own eyes seen bestowed.

Certain persons who appear very greedy are bent less on having than on not not-having.

Beware the man who refuses to accept what he deserves; he is paying himself back elsewhere.

X., great victim of the infinite, doesn't forget to arrange for a red tie before he sets off to rot. . . .

There is surely some childishness in the taste for greatness.

Working as we do for nothingness, we all more or less resemble those insects that, in obedience to dumb instinct, obstinately lay their eggs in gutted nests.

Knowing the precariousness of all human glory does not quench the ambitious man's longing to excel: he wants his place among those who make the crime of nothingness more evident.

IX

Death—the only thing greater than the word that names it . . .

All the days darkened in advance by misfortune, like the leaves of an ink-stained calendar.

To tell oneself one will never again see a certain being . . . A sensory anguish, comparable to that of a man suddenly stricken with blindness.

How does suffering manage to be at once uninterrupted and yet always reborn entirely new?

Suffering is the most living thing in the universe, for nothing else so resists any conception of its ending.

127

The night of suffering falls upon us brusquely, without twilight.

Occasionally suffering lets us off—but like a paroled prisoner.

Unquestionably suffering goes further than anything else —but toward what?

The one thing from which the sufferer may derive some comfort: having put a great deal of suffering behind him.

Increased courage often means not having even enough energy left to complain.

The recharging of one's soul with misery, each morning . . .

Those who have not really suffered do not know the comfort of the tolerable.

One can fairly well measure the love one has for another being by the quantity of suffering he is able to neutralize.

128

A single remedy—if one can use it: to love with more strength than one suffers.

One does not defeat suffering: all one can hope is that occasionally the game will be a draw.

The worst distress admits philosophizing: that is still to the point.

If we could make use of human suffering, there would be no need of any other source of energy.

In order to suffer less, *become* suffering. . . .

After every misfortune something like a curious inner molting of the soul occurs.

However much experience we may have gathered in this domain, it is still impossible to foresee what a being will become for us once we have lost him.

At first it is we who want to escape from a memory; later, it is the memory that escapes from us.

One can love perfectly only what one has lost forever.

Certain of the dead, more than others, teach us death.

Those one has failed to love enough during their lives—after their deaths one will have to love them a little too much.

The newly dead as he descends into our memory cannot help disturbing those who have preceded him. They protest; and thus unfolds in us a silent argument of shades.

We do not think about our own death so long as we love people older than ourselves: are we not called on to survive before we die?

Each of the persons we have loved carries off with him a little of our secret being.

One ought not to let grief break through the walls. One will heal in time—but too late if the icy wind has entered in.

Always meager in its joys, munificent in pain, *c'est la vie* . . .

Once the nerve centers of happiness have been damaged, a man can know only segmentary joys.

I have never said one could not have courage in facing life—I merely said it was needed.

After a certain point in existence, the only gaieties left are sacrileges.

A single misery floors us; several may keep us upright.

He who cannot cure may perhaps be able to resuscitate.

The multiplicity of wounds lends something unforeseen to our plight; we don't know which we are going to choose to suffer from.

I should not know myself without my griefs.

There may be a sort of relief in suffering from something out of the common run of one's miseries.

However scarred we already may be, life, when it wants to wound us again, will easily know where to find an un-bruised spot.

What you fear will not take place; something worse will.

Luckily our griefs sometimes overshadow one another.

There are people who go through life in a constant in-toxication of pain: always existing between two deaths, as others between two drinks.

To love life would be to love uprooting.

A life that discharges an excess of pain in its course is a bad chemical mixture.

An essential constant of the human being: his capacity for pain.

How many deaths must we live to learn that we shall die?

As I move closer to the dead they seem to me to grow a bit less sacred.

The tragic quality of life does not come from underground.

One can't have much leaning for sadness if one dares make merry without fear of what may happen when the party is over.

There are times when one would fear a new grief less than a happiness one might not know what to do with.

Merciful daily sleepwalking. I fear all that wakens and undeceives.

You cannot compare two sorrows unless you have equal insight.

To live is often to struggle toward goals one has no desire to reach.

Suffering is the most efficient way of feeling life: it overrates existence even while marking it with a minus sign.

It is no help to know that our suffering depends on certain chemical reactions that take place in our brain.

Don't, in order to avoid suffering, waste even the least bit of the strength required to meet it.

Pain will avenge itself without delay upon the least infidelity: respite must be sought not outside it, but within.

Not even the slightest respite is possible until suffering can reach the point where it no longer has strength to cling to its object.

Even more than thought, suffering can create an illusion of permanence: this pain that permeates our being—is it possible that some part of it will not last even in our scattered bones?

Faithfulness to the dead is the best way of insulting life.

I fear all change, even for the better: casting a new light on life, it might suddenly make it intolerable.

All would be well for the wise were it possible to draw any conclusion from the fact of universal human suffering; but things are not quite so simple as they are cruel.

That the last act be "always bloody"—I can take that, if I must. But that it has been necessary throughout the whole comedy to be spattered with the blood of the other victims . . .

To free oneself of a sorrow one must absorb and incorporate it. No consolation except at one's own expense.

In the loss of those we love, it is less their life that escapes us than their death that invades.

One can have got over a sorrow without having grown accustomed to it: memory of it is merely laid aside. But if one stumbles on it again by chance, it will have lost none of its fury.

Our dead from time to time rise up in us with sudden and mysterious replenishment of life.

Let us be grateful for the chaos of life: it diverts us from the horror.

I should have been grateful for the existence of things worth sacrificing pleasure to.

There is no intelligent happiness.

Human life does not deserve to be adorned: it is a meager scenario whose poverty is accentuated by trimmings.

Life has become second nature to us.

I am not very demanding in private matters; it is another universe that I require.

X

What people call a responsible man is one who is only as irresponsible as everybody else.

The most horrendous of guilty humans is no less innocent than the universe.

We absolve the human machine if it commits evil when functioning poorly; we condemn it for the same thing if it is in good shape.

Morality of the geneticist: evil is dominant, good recessive.

An authentic monster disturbs the natural order less than a flawed hero.

Morality is what is left of fear forgotten.

"Why do you do that?" "For a God who might be like me."

How much ugliness we carry about in us, of which a very slight lapse of attention would have spared us ever becoming aware!

Chemistry of remorse: memory of error cannot be dissolved except in an excess of pain.

How fine it is to yield first place to something there is no glory in preferring to oneself!

Virtue is most itself when it does not bear that name.

The less one has of God, the more one must believe in Him.

I denounce men's evil, and at the same time marvel that it goes no further.

I am, by and large, ungifted for ordinary wickedness; my worst behavior is more personal.

We are so constructed that we should like renunciation to qualify us for possession.

The virtue we prize most highly is the one that has in it a capacity for not being virtuous.

Though good may be infinitely meritorious, evil cannot be infinitely faulty.

He who commits a crime is less guilty than He who is supposed to have created both crime and remorse.

Every man is my brother as long as he keeps his mouth shut.

Certain acts of daring are reserved for those who have managed to take precautions.

I hate uncourageous courage, prideless pride.

I often find it hard to repress a certain indulgence toward those who have aroused everybody's scorn. Weren't there, after all, a great many ways by which they might have become what they are, with honor?

I hear people say: "We need fine ideals," in the same tone as they might say: "We need good financial standing."

There is in X. much moral prinkery.

The ignoble thing is not men's base behavior, but the ways in which they get their pardons.

Men, for the most part, deserve one another.

Living has not taught me much about men, but what I knew of them before I now know better.

How easily one would pass for a good man if one could agree to express what one *almost* feels.

We are the only ones who know all that goes to make up our good conduct.

There is sometimes much merit in not making use of one's detachment.

Whatever reproach the man in me makes to the man, the animal cannot fail to pity the animal.

Nothing rouses one so to virtue as the lapses of those who make a profession of it.

It is excessive to bet on two numbers; it is excessive to bet even on one.

Society produces reactions in me that make me dislike myself. I prefer myself alone.

I approve out of weariness, I contradict out of impatience.

I am not one of those who can form a good impression of themselves when talking to themselves; my inner speech is more brutal than my thought.

Chance in life is almost always motivated, and that is why I am deliberately severe toward it.

The most interesting thing about a human being is the connection between his worst and best sides.

Physically we were all monsters before birth. And morally, too, for a rather long time after it.

La Rochefoucauld and Babinski both exaggerate: not everything is pretense, either in virtue or in hysteria.

Psychoanalysis has taught us that man is a wolf, not only toward his neighbor but toward himself, as well.

I am less ashamed of my basic feelings than of my surface ones.

Error is not so much the doing of evil as doing it so un-necessarily.

All sorts of thoughts run through us, no doubt, but the soul is not deceived: it has subtle scales to detect as they pass the ones that weigh too heavily upon it.

Prevented from knowing even a single stranger-soul, how shall we measure our own? We shall vanish without having found out who we are.

We do not regret having done evil—merely having done it so awkwardly that we feel remorse.

How is it possible to bear what remorse has finally done with our faults?

I have no memory except for my weaknesses. Remorse, accessory to remembrance.

There are stainable souls: the least thing spots them.

The only liberty life concedes us is to choose our own regrets.

Being good is not the hard thing; what is, is being so under the conditions life imposes.

I don't put much stock in actions; there are worse things.

How much of oneself one must reject in order to remain oneself!

I no longer even desire all that I know I shall not get.

143

In self-detachment, one cuts oneself off as well from others.

One sometimes needs a little more than one deserves.

The universe does not take on sense except in proportion as one cuts it down—as with those cipher messages that have to be interpreted by covering up certain letters. Each man has his own key.

It seems to us that others have nothing more important to do than trying to be happy.

Tomorrow will decide whether our dubious today should be imputed to misfortune or good.

One has always been less unhappy than one thinks—just as one has always slept better.

All the traits people reproach in me are the ones I reproach myself with not having enough of.

I hate futility, but do so knowing that nothing matters.

Consolation: you could be the same person—and satisfied!

Don't put off disdain until they have bruised you: it would come too late.

No one outdoes me in being at once unsure of being right and incapable of changing my mind.

I prefer finding myself rather than someone else in the wrong; the interest is much livelier.

The trouble with truth is that it is too much like what the opponent thinks.

To hold an opinion is to prefer to be wrong in a certain sense.

We hold less by being right than by the freedom to be wrong.

We fight the more bitterly in others what we have already defeated in ourselves.

Moral courage is being able, if necessary, to humble one's favorite self.

It may offend us to hear our own thoughts expressed by others: we are not sure enough of their souls.

To reflect is to disturb one's thoughts.

Socially I am interested only in the value of a few and in the suffering of all.

The desire for social equality is not unmixed with a certain eagerness to be rid of the bother of pity.

I should have no use for a paradise in which I should be deprived of the right to prefer hell.

The energy of the atom will be unleashed, people will travel among the stars, life will be prolonged, tuberculosis and cancer will be cured, but we won't find the secret of government by the least unworthy.

Is it the exercise of power that corrupts men, or is it that corruptible temperaments are naturally suited to the exercise of power? Same problem as for the mole: has it got small eyes because it lives underground, or does it live underground because its eyes are small?

The least one can say of power is that a vocation for it is suspicious.

In politics, yesterday's lie is attacked only to flatter today's.

To want to be governed by pure men is to want to be governed by albinos or hexadactyls.

We are not naïve enough to ask for pure men; we ask merely for men whose impurity does not conflict with the obligations of their job.

In politics the fools can bring it about that the wise be wrong.

A good partisan must be able to take the requirements of strategy for the claims of justice.

I don't judge a regime by the damning criticism of the opposition, but by the ingenuous praise of the partisan.

I am too unsatisfied with myself to hope for a future that might satisfy me.

If one had a well-governed soul, there would be no need to silence the opposition in it.

Not even to smooth the way for the noblest progress can humanity free itself of certain scruples. If its burden were made too light, it would give up.

If each man is but the image of all—what solitude!

Either to annul oneself by isolation or to abase oneself by getting together.

It is something to the honor of the past to have fathered a present that condemns it.

My natural tendency is to oppose the current: like certain water bugs I have negative "rheotropism."

It is always by accident that the several ideas we cherish meet in reality.

As one marches toward the future one can always keep one's face a little averted.

I am always hardest on the lies that offer to support my ideas: weren't those ideas big enough to manage by themselves?

If a clever advertising campaign were to announce that ipecac is an aid to digestion, we would soon see men eating it without vomiting.

The human brain: that sponge all ready to soak up every lie . . .

A thousand hurts are worth more than one hurt; a thousand thoughts are not always worth one thought.

It is easier to die for what one believes than to believe in it a little less.

When they denounce the adversary, how do they manage not to recognize his voice in their own throats?

Men's opinions are discredited by their reflexes.

149

Hatred, for the man who is not engaged in it, is a little like the odor of garlic for one who hasn't eaten any.

Many men would have known how to hate even if they had never heard of hatred.

I fear faith; it leads to acts. *Autos-da-fé* . . .

Can't men be given enough to live on without at the same time being given the desire to kill one another?

Stupidity, outrage, vanity, cruelty, iniquity, bad faith, falsehood—we fail to see the whole array when it is facing in the same direction as we.

It is rare for truth to contain anything to suit the passions.

It is almost as impossible for many of us to show any esteem for those who do not share our beliefs as for an infant to use its arms separately.

It is a bitter law that would have every victory over another carry with it a personal loss. Just how much must one agree to offend against an inner ideal for the sake of defending an external one?

There is no greater crime against the mind than giving a bad conscience to truth.

To find the same act either splendid or ignoble according to who has dictated it, to excoriate falsehood in one place and glorify it elsewhere, to let clothes, color, looks determine whether one accuses or excuses, to praise force when it is one's accomplice and damn it when it is on the opposite side: these are things I do not know how to do and am in no hurry to learn. . . .

There are moments when very little truth would be enough to shape opinion. One might be hated at extremely low cost.

In order to remain true to oneself one ought to renounce one's party three times a day.

Would you really care for the existence on earth of an ideal in which you recognized your own features?

Far too often the choices reality proposes are such as to take away one's taste for choosing.

151

Sometimes I overrate the courage of those whose thought is in opposition to my own: are they not challenging the only opinion that counts in my view?

Nobody wants to make himself a target for hatred, even for the sake of all the truths.

For a man who knows himself well, having an opinion might itself be a reason for doubting it.

Don't buy ideas in a bull market.

Humanity is certainly larger than any of the ideals it has forged for itself; but maybe, in order to progress, it has need of those "fetishists" who can cling to just one.

It is easy for those who lack any deep convictions to pick out at any given moment the one best suited to reality.

There is nothing discouraging in thinking ill of humanity. The hope of seeing the wickedness of all men operate for the profit of all is really rather fine.

Let those who boast of their stand against violence sometimes consider all that apparent gentleness may cover up—and that the cleanness of their hands depends entirely on the patience of those they crush. . . .

One may find oneself pretending to share certain mistakes in preference to parting company with the people one differs with least.

Fear of the new, distrust of life . . . What is beautiful enough to do without the old lighting?

It is not the newborn world that frightens me, but, sometimes, the faces of those who are delivering it.

Lucky are those who believe in something strongly enough to think that all means are justified in reaching it.

Nowadays credulity seeks its authorization from the future, not the past. People do not say: "Our fathers believed in it," but: "Our sons are going to believe in it."

"Will he be any happier for being educated and enlightened?" say those who want to close the gates of culture to the masses. That is not the question. Ought one to stop infants from growing up on the pretext that children

153

are happier than men? The growth of humankind is directed rather to *more-being* than to *well-being*, and, I should decidedly not be surprised if suffering were to increase in the social world as does entropy in the universe.

Clearly the ideal situation would be that in which society would increasingly respect the individual, who would, in turn, increasingly respect society.

A future one has talked too much about becomes as boring as a past.

I, whose whole life has been based on a few people, and for whom the meaning of the universe has been bound up in a small number of faces, cry out with my whole mind for the time when the individual will be compelled to attach himself to vaster and less ephemeral objects.

Static morale is the hard thing. It is easier to lead men to death than to help them to live where they are.

Politics asks us to judge complex inequalities into which enter not merely numerous unknowns, but incommensurable values. What a lot we are forced to take for granted in order to reach even a passable solution of these —and with what scorn for consistency!

War: millions of corpses laid out to form the most repulsive of all things—history.

Either the human point of view or else that of Sirius: I find it hard to locate myself between the two, and I recoil from seeing a man give his all for what the star values at nothing.

Between the loftiest idea and the humblest human life lies an unbridgeable gap that only the good will of·a hero can fill.

It is the destiny of every war eventually to seem less necessary than at the moment it was agreed on.

There will always be enough men to think that whole peoples should be sacrificed to wisps of some ideal; and I admit that I have no hesitation in ranging myself with those who would pay any price to save the largest possible mass of human protoplasm.

People won't admit that a war could have been avoided until the moment arrives for crying up another.

The ignoble face of war always knows how to change its make-up.

Nothing human is worth much blood.

The consequences of human struggles are necessarily unpredictable, and no one is clever enough to guess exactly where his victory will lead him.

Resolved problems, said Descartes, are battles won. . . . But won battles are not resolved problems.

The farce of rights might end by making us less stern about the drama of force.

Force takes precedence over right, and money over force.

It is altogether exceptional for a man to be a pacifist for more than one war.

Every war is a civil war, the pacifists of olden times used to say in order to arouse distaste for fighting. Today we hear the same thing said with the object of arousing appetite.

People who have no hesitation in letting blood flow more freely than we would dare let water flow . . .

Human ugliness stands out sharply against a background of blood.

In the service of more and more elevated ideals, men go on further and further debasing themselves.

Human ideas, no less fierce than nature . . .

Impossible to count on the exhaustion of nations to make peace lasting; unfortunately for humans, the gigantic organisms of which they are part continually increase their power of regeneration.

Peace will never be desired for itself, it can only be an epiphenomenon.

Among naturalists engaged in classifying living things, there are two opposing positions: one group chooses to underline the differentiating characteristics of organic types, and are thus known as "separatists"; the other group, or "unifiers," prefers to emphasize affinity, likeness. In human affairs my place is with the second group: it is instinctive with me to deny difference, and if it is pointed out to me I deny that it is essential.

Our way of judging events depends on the point of departure we have chosen.

Innumerable deaths and inestimable suffering—this is the terrifying ransom that the future demands of the present in every century. What waste and what useless sacrifice! But one never settles one's debts with the irresponsible and elusive future.

Everyone has his share of greed; if so-and-so appears disinterested it is merely because he doesn't care for what is usually prized.

I become less severe toward class prejudices and the claims of the privileged when I see they are dependent on reflexes or instincts. I exculpate the man through the animal.

I am more inclined to find the animal in man than to seek man in the animal.

I feel a notable degree of repugnance toward those streams of altruism that burst forth from overfed egoisms.

Speaking cruelties gives more relief than inflicting them; action is less effective than words.

One can make oneself understood by those who do not speak the same language, but not by those for whom words do not have the same sense.

Before every argument there should be an understanding: are two opinions to be confronted, two minds to be measured, or two souls to clash?

I refuse to enter into discussion with those I feel to be less sensitive to truth than I.

What is the use of tickling certain people with a truth when one cannot smite them with full force?

In discussion, learn to quit at the first "true," as one would in a duel at the first drawing of blood.

Disputes of hate or disputes of love: one tries either to clarify differences or to diminish them. Both purposes are equally futile.

Why be irritated even by an "unstable" mind if one's own is perfectly sound?

There are times when mutual understanding with our fellow man would be impossible unless we could make him live our own past life.

There is a degree of tolerance that borders on insult.

How refreshing, from time to time, to admire contrary to one's taste, to judge against one's convictions, to be impassioned against one's ideal!

I am grateful to those who, by their opposition, often help me to remain true to myself.

The proper revenge against the scorn of a fool would be to cause him to be scorned by a greater fool than he.

X. and Y. are for once in full agreement: from converse premises they have drawn inverse conclusions.

Intelligence is certainly not to blame if imbeciles try to apply it where it is uncalled for.

Human opinion would be quite different if everyone would risk his own: fear prevents some people from including themselves in the poll.

We suffer from a strange need to make our thoughts perfectly clear to those who are certain to interpret them the more inaccurately in proportion as we have stated them clearly.

To show oneself in one's true colors is to agree to be seen otherwise. How reckon the "distortion" our image undergoes in another mind?

We do not need others to believe that we are what we really are.

The man who thought nothing but what must be thought would win no one over: truth has no disciples.

Do not believe yourself in moments of anger, said a sage. But anger pre-exists in the state of calm. Never believe yourself.

Distrust everything you think a little too forcefully.

What ultimately matters is not an opinion but its altitude. However you happen to think, suspect that there must be a loftier way of thinking differently.

To be objective is to value one's judgment more than any object.

One has of course the right to change opinion, but on condition of not fraudulently adjusting the new to the old.

It is not yet quite clear whether we make more mistakes by judging according to the in- or the out-sides of things.

The only thoughts we may be sure we shall think are those we should prefer not to.

I do not like to hear what I cherish or respect talked about; words can disgust me with anything.

Often what I fear in others is the wind from outside that they bring with them.

Best proof of the adversary's iniquity is our own.

The place to which the unjust accusations of the adversary would consign us may be one we have no desire whatsoever to occupy.

When reason turns out to be right, folly has already moved elsewhere.

Nobody adjusts himself to reality like the man who has understood once for all that he can't be satisfied with it.

One can judge man only by the measure of man, and to denounce humanity is merely to point out its margin of variation.

Better not impute to a few what pertains to humanity, nor to humanity what pertains to a few.

He who is nowhere at ease will prefer the place where, at least, he can give free rein to his discomfort.

A lie may be less false than a carefully chosen truth.

In order to estimate a man's courage one must know what his fears are.

Reason's weakness is the belief that it has the capacity to convince unreason.

Nothing so incites to airs of dignity as the consciousness of refraining from evil.

One sometimes wonders which is more the case: that men are unworthy to be told the truth or that one fears them enough to lie to them.

Pity must hurry if it wants to arrive before scorn.

Our psychology is founded on a very few beings: better make a good choice of whom to love or whom to hate.

To have many friends is to diversify one's boredom.

The bad part of hurting someone is giving him better insight into oneself.

The kindnesses of others sometimes incline one to be reconciled with egoism.

It takes extremely little to make us self-indulgent, and very often what we dislike extremely is what, without being us, resembles us.

We have all momentarily resembled one of the people we find most repulsive.

It is a kind of vice to prefer being oneself to being right.

I am hungry only for my truth.

All one imagines one wants because it is impossible— and all one doesn't know one wants because it is impossible . . .

He who is too gentle in action sometimes finds it very difficult not to be too severe in thought.

165

What a miserable client I am for the universe! And how many things one could remove from it without doing me any injury!

All that deprives us exempts us.

How few things seem beautiful enough to make up for the trouble of looking at them!

All accessory satisfactions make us still more subject to essential torments.

To use death against life, and life against death . . .

Things whose vanity we feel at the very moment of doing them. Others whose vanity we will know tomorrow, or in ten years. And still others whose vanity we will still not know, even at the hour of our death . . .

Reward of pessimism. How many times I would have been tempted to call out to some moment: stay! you are so lovely through not being more repulsive. . . .

Life teaches us ferocity without showing us how to use it.

Altruism is often an alibi.

My way of living gives me more assurance of being right than does my way of thinking.

The longer one lives, the less enthusiasm one puts into repairing one's losses: for what coming wound is it worth forming scar tissue?

What can happiness possibly consist in, unless in not being too unhappy among misfortunes?

It is more difficult to make peace with the whole of one soul than to be satisfied with only one body.

We hold a grudge against those who make us choose between wounding them and renouncing ourselves.

Life is almost as disagreeable with those one *doesn't* care for.

There are times when everything we dislike in a person becomes perceptible, like all the minutest blood vessels of an animal into which a dye has been injected.

It is cheating those we love, to let others make us suffer.

Almost nobody is worth the hurt one causes oneself when one wounds him.

How much one must love a person to prefer him to his absence!

Were it not for missing the others, each of the people I love would be enough to fill my need; even one is too many for me.

Any ugliness is more desirable than the beauty with which one is satiated.

One can forgive a person for a few moments as one pardons a book for a few lines.

A good marriage is one in which each of the two persons has the luck of being able to bear the other's unbearablenesses.

A little heart is enough to get in the way.

Pity the man who cannot press another creature to his breast without being made uncomfortable by the scent of the unknown soul. . . .

With those we are resolved to love no matter what they do to us—when we come to the point of resenting this, there is nothing for it but to love them even more.

Don't leave it to spite to disclose the truth about the person you love.

I love myself only when I prefer someone else.

One does not love a person at all if one does not know how much one could, if need be, hate him.

Two sure things: one becomes more intelligent every day, and one loves more deeply those one loves.

Those who love us would sometimes resent us if they knew for what reasons we forgive them.

The chronic irritation of jealousy ends by making benign loves malignant.

We hold it against others when their resentment forces us to reconsider our mistakes.

Imagination has its limits. It is reality that is inexhaustible: one is never done with a memory.

An excess of frankness can lead to falsehood just as an excess of gentleness to cruelty.

Sensitivity declines rapidly in those who live with heart bared.

Certain men imagine that they feel all the lofty sentiments of which they can conceive.

How many people ask themselves: what, under the present circumstances, ought he-who-I-am to think?

One can often measure the true nobility of an individual by the number of not quite noble feelings he allows to be seen.

To hate fatigues.

He who asks too little of life will always be disappointed by it.

Where my fellow man is concerned, I always judge like the most malevolent, but with benevolence.

People are quick to call those who do not use others for their own advancement egotists.

There is no word in any language for that which deserves loyalty.

Life almost never asks us for the sacrifices that would suit us.

Things succeed through their baser qualities, endure through their higher.

171

One always postpones the time for living, and I quit my prey to step into the shade quite as though I did not know it was the shade. . . .

How really narrow it is, the interval between the too doubtful and the too sure!

At first one merely asks things to be possible, and then one reproaches them with not being impossibly perfect.

Human neoteinia: a man who reaches adulthood and still preserves certain illusions makes one think of those Mexican salamanders that keep the gills of the larval stage until they reach full growth.

A man thinks himself happy when he thinks he has set his course toward what he thinks he loves.

The only valuable things are those one does not have to believe in in order to live by them.

What arises from instinct agrees to be goalless.

It is not enough to desire; in addition one must not know too clearly what it is one desires.

The longer one lives, the less importance one attaches to things, and also the less importance to importance.

Without warning life breaks into what one might call long moments of silence.

To covet everything is, in the last analysis, not to covet anything. Such avidity can only come from lack of real lacks.

The need for absolutes may be nothing but a want of love.

Try to give enough meaning to small details to be able to forget the futility of the wholes.

Life little by little dislodges us from everywhere.

Would it not indeed be the most astonishing of all prodigies if, one day, the inert mountain did give birth to a living mouse?

No happiness resembles what one imagines when one is prevented from experiencing any happiness.

To live is to play puss-in-the-corner with one's griefs.

Very little would have been enough for me had it been pure.

A Biologist's Notebook

Spring, for the biologist.

Season of pollens, seeding, mating, nuptial liveries. Cellular effusion, tissue swellings, flux of hormones, dispersion of gametes, mingling of chromosomes, germinal hurly-burly.

Nature's electoral period, when she makes secret choice of tomorrow's representatives.

Living on intimate terms with nature, one inadvertently becomes different from other people. Her silent language penetrates, saturates, persuades one gently of the insufficiency of all human speech.

To listen to the philosophers, wouldn't one say they were candidates for an examination in which it was thought better to make any answer whatsoever than to remain silent?

Sixtieth year.

The old man's disguise I am going to be forced to put on . . .

I am reaching the age when, if a man is poor, people feel sorry for him.

A man is not old as long as he is seeking something.

Though it may not have an answer for everything, science will, perhaps, give us a remedy for everything.

One cannot stop unfair critics, but one can, by one's work, try to make them even more unfair.

Too many opponents—or not enough of them.
The solitude of being one, and that of being the only one.

There is no philosophic word that can soothe me, but I know of none that can make me see red.

A certain master of thought suddenly becomes aware of what has been staring everybody in the face for years. Does he admit that he has been blind until now? Not at all: in his view, what he has just seen ought not to have been seen before.

The heroism of the victims spatters the torturers with blood.

178

On the tally sheet of evil that may be imputed to every form of sectarianism, we must enter, first, all the good it does to sectarianism of the opposite camp.

In politics it is easier to be a prophet than a judge.

If a true scientist wanted to commit fraud, what a great life he would have—for a while.
The same holds for a true artist.

Reason has its troubles that the heart knows nothing of.

Nothing gets omitted like essentials.

The problem of freedom has nothing to do with man. It is God's affair, exclusively.

I am sometimes uncertain whether I care for biology because it is the science of life or care for life because it is the subject of biology.

Intellectual honesty is the only quality one cannot sham.

All that can serve truth can likewise serve falsehood.

The flexibility of fanaticism only helps to diversify its crimes.

The nobility of a human being is strictly independent of that of his convictions.

To be ever ready to become one's own heresiarch.

My vanity is for internal consumption.

If they exalt me, I lower myself; if they place me low, I set myself high. I fight for everything I am denied; I feel I am unworthy of all that is granted me.

Rather than a sorcerer's apprentice, man is a god in spite of himself. There is no school for teaching god-skills.

I am too passionately devoted to peace to be always on the pacifists' side.

Am I, after all, vainer than everybody else? I who ask for nothing but renown minus all its advantages!

Doctrinaire criticism: always ill-founded.

Rejected in the name of vitalism: phagocytosis, the idea of the organizer, the chromosomal theory of heredity, etc.

If there is anything of which I am sure, it is that this is not the last time we shall have seen truth frowned on in the name of principle.

The only images which will never lose luster for me: were I to live a thousand years I should still be as deeply moved to see a frog's egg at the moment of segmentation, a salamander's embryo trembling under its diaphanous covering. . . .

A body of work such as Pasteur's is inconceivable in our time: no one man would be given a chance to create a whole science. Nowadays a path is scarcely opened up when the crowd begins to pour in.

To love an idea is to love it a little more than one should.

The best truths are disinclined to attract disciples.

The divine is perhaps that quality in man which permits him to endure the lack of God.

If God existed, there would be no wicked men—only clumsy ones.

One reads the book of a dead author, not to judge him but to be nourished by him.

It is in this way that I should like to be read.

"You suffer too much. . . ." "Nonsense; it never hurts to suffer."

Differences between one man and another? Of course—but not so sharp that they aren't blotted out, for me, the moment one of us sets himself up to judge another.

Marxist assurance.

What have they ever understood, explained, clarified, invented, since they acquired those famous keys that neither Claude Bernard nor Pasteur, nor Darwin, nor Mendel, nor Freud, nor Einstein possessed?

Is it possible in our century for good minds seriously to believe that Marx and Engels have articulated once and for all the laws of thought and matter?

Everything of any worth, all that counts in science—it cannot be said too often—has been built up apart from doctrinaire concerns. It is all too easy for anyone who knows a little about the history of biology to imagine what the position of the Marxists would have been at the time of the great, opinion-splitting disputes. How often they would have had to take the wrong side in order to follow their principles! They would have supported Pouchet against Pasteur in the quarrel over spontaneous generation, Berthelot against Pasteur in the debate over alcoholic fermentation, and so on.

Dare we conjecture that Marxism refrained from making its appearance in the world until its influence was likely to be harmless for the mind?

Pluralism of truth.

Beware, above all, the single party in science; know there are no rules for being right.

Nothing repels me as much as the tendentious insinuations of the partisan.

I prefer an ear in full view to a peeking lobe.

It is infinitely painful to be compelled by the demands of intelligence to fight what most people fight only through poverty of heart.

Certainly it is sometimes necessary to silence one's scruples—but beware the peril of dismissing them in advance!

To be capable of simplifying questions, but also of restoring their complexity.

For those who find austerity congenial, duty may lie in pleasure.

I avoid discussion with those who are incapable of wronging themselves by their thoughts.

The trivialities of a great mind interest me more than the treasures of a mediocre one.

Minor joys of the magician: to see quivering in an aquarium larvae that would not have been born but for human intervention.

My day has not been wasted: I have heard for the first time the delicate clicking of the Xenopus.

In his fine book, *L'Anxiété de Lucrèce*, Dr. Logre finds a connection between the Latin poet's materialism and his morbid fear of life. Profoundly melancholic and eager to be done with the discomfort of being, Lucretius, saw in survival only a cruel prolongation of anguish. I, however, am not quite sure that the individual always selects the philosophy that matches his most deep-seated feelings. There are some who think with Lucretius but feel with Pascal. Baffled by nothingness, yet incapable of rejecting the idea of it, they take the soul to be "no more than a little wind and smoke," but say so dejectedly, as though it were "the saddest thing in the world."

All that certain people ask is that they be authorized to deify nonbeing.

The inverse symmetry of a mirror image brings out the flaws of the mirrored. Satire follows a similar method.

How often we sacrifice today to a tomorrow which will be quite capable of making us take our sacrifice back.

My incapacities safeguard me.

If I feel any lurking doubt about the source of an action of mine, it is my habit to choose the least honorable paternity.

Incapable of any self-deception on my own account, I am one of those who know what they think before they have thought it.

Insensitive? Certainly not; but not so naïve as to let you see where you've wounded me.

Vacations? Aren't there enough miseries to interrupt us during the course of the year?

Travel?
Life is not worth stirring up.

I disdain the transitory exactly as though I believed in the eternal.

If everything in the universe is thought, then thought is a pretty trivial thing.

Luckily, there is no future life. If there were, we should see the very same fellows making themselves agreeable up above.

I can only be strong in order to protect my weaknesses.

I reproach history with being conjectural; but, to tell the truth, I should find it just as annoying if I could think it determinate.

The only witnesses I trust are those who would not let themselves be hanged.

It is unusual to be so entirely wrong as to be forced to admit it.

Cheat the future, and the present will take its cut.

It is dangerous for either ideas or friends to get on our nerves, even momentarily: we notice their weaknesses.

At times one feels something like homesickness for one's moral antipodes.

The worst monotony is the kind that comes of diversity.

Maxims.
For a reflection printed between two blank spaces to leave me cold, its dullness must be sensational.

In art the most dangerous models are those there is least risk in imitating.

Some residue is always left in us of the trivial slanders our hearts have indulged in about those we love.

I tend to rate as courageous the deed I would by no means do, but it is not necessarily courage if others do it.

"There is no greater mental disorder than to believe things because one desires them to be." (Bossuet) My own disorder would rather be to deny them because I wish they were.

Laboratory.

Even when one achieves nothing, one smells the odor of truth in hiding.

The sadness of anniversaries, were one already consoled!

I almost always refuse what is offered me, but still my vanity is stirred. Would it not be better to accept, and without emotion?

Overheard: a stout woman talking with harsh self-assurance about workmen. I resent such soft bodies issuing hard words.

The world, just as ephemeral as a fair . . .

For anyone with the slightest delicacy of nose, what is there in these parts that doesn't give off a scent of corpse?

Writer X. expresses his vanity with such precision that one would be tempted to call his absurdity talented.

From the instant thought made its appearance, the damage was done: chemical reactions ought not to have ended in questions.

One is always justified in hating the adversary—as one sees him.

I want to be able to read a scientific book without finding the names of Marx and Engels on every page.

After childhood one should know, once and for all, that nothing makes sense.

Go ahead, grant yourself, in thought, everything you deserve. . . . And, in addition, everything you could possibly get, without being too indecent, even if you don't deserve it . . . And, furthermore, all that the best of the best deserve . . .
It is nothing.

I have difficulty in believing in the great roles in life, especially if they are well played.

How few things there are in a life that are made for it!

The lowest cowardice: to make use of what one does not love against what one loves.

Too easy, fine deeds.
Learn to perform some ugly ones, too, when necessary.

Choose? Isn't one cluttered enough with all one has not chosen?

Were I satisfied with myself, I should dislike myself.

Anger and desire accustom us to the discontinuity of being.

A double and parallel series—happiness and sorrow.
A man composes himself one past or another, according to their variations.

He who might deserve a God would perhaps have no need of one.

I should have liked life to have been a serious matter.

Notebook: a good deal of white space for nothing.

Even in the weakness of the moment I find it hard not to see menacing signs of a future strength.

Every war is a product of two parents; and those who lay all the blame on one side resemble the old-school naturalists who attributed the foetus to a single germ cell.

To be silent when one feels that one differs from others to the point where one could only collide with them fruitlessly.

All the blood it will take to wipe out what has just been written with blood . . .

It is annoying that in order to accomplish very little one has to think about it too much.

Learn to be satisfied with the momentary, the precarious, the changeable, the approximate, the uncertain, the insufficient, the impure. . . .

There are honorable intoxications which stand witness to customary sobriety.

Quotations—always inexact. I don't trust people who cannot even copy out.

Certain brief sentences are peerless in their ability to give one the feeling that nothing remains to be said.

Self-scrutiny.
I think I am one of those who can manage not to take on a completely different appearance under their own glance.

When the ideal shifts, one must change one's perspective.
The sunflower remains faithful to the sun.

Much baseness, also, fails.

It takes a very deep-rooted opinion to survive unexpressed.

Evil—all the more repugnant for being imbedded in the good . . .

I cannot live either with my griefs or without them.

A man is certainly compelled to believe in what he does when he gets no profit out of it.

It is the mark of a very rare sort of virtue not to want to make use of its nobility.

The man who learns hatred must already have known it.

There are some persons we could not cut down to size without diminishing ourselves as well.

Occasionally we prefer to stay at a distance from those who think differently from ourselves, so much should we itch to agree with them.

Rarely, when one despises something to excess, does one escape prizing it to excess sometime later.

Many men of science start philosophizing late in the day. I have reversed the direction. The longer I go on, the more I turn away from broad syntheses to apply myself to patient analyses.
I am more and more in love with fact.

For an artist, an excess of taste can be lethal.

It is possible that the individual may find his profit and even his well-being in giving himself up to the group, but he can do so only to the latter's detriment. For its sake, not his own, he must resist it.

It is important that everything about a style give the impression of being intentional—and perhaps chiefly the weaknesses.

Think roughshod; change shoes to write.

Contempt of public opinion leads to contempt for honors. But an even greater contempt . . .

God, that checkroom of our dreams . . .

I like sentences so tight that a single syllable can exert its power.

In what has razed us, seek the stuff for rebuilding.

Assassination committed by nature: like it or not, one has got to leave this life stunned, or strangled, or bled, or poisoned. . . .

The unpredictable part of a still living, still evolving sorrow.
Beware the second wind of suffering.

Prerequisite for rereadability in books: that they be forgettable.

The infinite and sterile fertility of the human mind.

X. is magnanimous, isn't he? He forgives his friends all the villainies he attributes to them.

We are sometimes discouraged when we read minor writers, but also encouraged sometimes when we read the great.

To say of men that they are bad is to say they are worse than we think we are, or worse than the ideal man whose image we have built up on the basis of a certain few.

It is not easy to imagine how little interested a scientist usually is in the work of any other, with the possible exception of the teacher who backs him or the student who honors him.

Man and nature.
All that man does and nature cannot do.
All that nature does and man cannot do.

Significance of life.
Life, like the work of art, means no more than it says.

There are certain moments when we might wish the future were built by men of the past.

Matter, since it transforms itself into energy, does not exist: thus, the soul does exist. This is how God is proven in the salons.

Indulgence toward others, stemming from lack of worldly ambition. I cannot manage to see them as competitors or rivals. I occupy another terrain—rather mysterious, even to me—which their threat does not reach.

That indefinable quality of every life which makes one accept life . . .

Writers for every type of reader: universal donors.

The ideal, without doubt, varies, but its enemies, alas, are always the same.

As I go on in life I tend to become less curious about myself. Soon not even my weaknesses will interest me.

There is much mystery in our choice of what seems to us worthy of note.

I am much too firmly attached to certain ideas, not to give myself credit when I feel disappointed in them.

Is it, in fact, man I am trying to study through the toad?
In any case, the toad interests me more than man.

Remorse? It would be impossible for me to feel any, save toward man or men.
One would always be too good for a God.

Renown? I've already got more of it than those I respect, and will never have as much as those for whom I feel contempt . . .

Before one has time to look at a face it has withered.

To be clear is to confess.

Mental automatism of partisans.

Possibly legitimate, even necessary, but difficult to accept for one who has a taste for vital spontaneity and unpredictability.

Out of the material of my one life, limited as it is, I could cut myself several existences each very different from my own, and each seemingly worthy of being lived.

If only for the sake of mental hygiene, let us be clearly aware of the accidental quality of our tastes, our opinions, our beliefs, and our unbeliefs.

Let us from time to time recall all the possible "I's" with whom we couldn't possibly get along.

The first to have lit a fire is not thereby responsible for all conflagrations.

Disintegration of the atom.

From now on, all animals, all plants, everything alive is at the mercy of human error or stupidity.

Scruple.

There are moments when one wonders whether, in disseminating science, one has done anything other than facilitate jargon.

The books that make us understand a science are not the ones that make us love it.

I love truth, and I have pity for human suffering. But it is not with such stuff that one forms a political opinion.

True, the word "void" has hardly more sense than the word "God." How should you expect the mouth of man to utter a word that could satisfy his mind?

Consolation.
If I were in every respect the man I should have longed to be, who would notice it?

Precocious ambition spoils style, falsifies tone.
I should like words spoken by someone who had never dreamt of being great.

All that is thought or felt with an eye to its expression is insignificant.

Afterlife?
It is the body that survives the mind, for several hours.

The detours of art.
Perseverance in something one ought not to have done sometimes leads to the discovery of what one ought indeed to do.

No work of the mind exists—book, theory, hypothesis—which may not be criticized either from above or below. And often is; both ways simultaneously.

It is already something of an achievement to achieve a perspective on one's misery that keeps it from being too detestable.

I have a predilection for a certain "neutrality" of style. But I am terribly demanding with respect to the quality of this "neuter."

Suffering, my oldest friend . . .

Let them exile thought if they must—but let them not conscript it.

A mutation is a lapsus, a misprint of life.
In order to discover the mutations of toads I make use of my trained proofreader's eyes.

There are people whose best side remains sterile, and others whose worst becomes fertile.

The great power of the Communists is that one can hardly criticize them without invoking their most thoroughly accepted ideal.

I consent to my suffering, provided it makes me better able to understand that of others.

To each his counter-void.
The thought of death glides past me when I look at certain faces or when I handle my toads.

I feel very optimistic about the future of pessimism.

On the problems that really trouble us, we should be ready to question the first comer.

I am always attracted by those who believe the things I refuse to believe. When it comes to being reasonable, I don't need anyone.

My life—simple, monotonous, linear, pure, *classical*: unity of place, unity of tone, unity of action.

The total absence of music in a style is perhaps preferable to an already familiar music.

Man's power grows more rapidly than his wisdom: this is what the biometrician calls an allometric increase.

When one is on the point of being sickened by man, it is well to think of some few men: the same beings who have made us too hard on the human will help us to remain faithful to it.

From everyone, or almost, I expect the worst—but in order to excuse it.

My diabolic mercifulness . . .

From those one does not care for, how benign is ingratitude!

Marxist dogmatism.

It is reactionary of him, someone affirms, not to believe in the inheritance of acquired characteristics.

I will never admit that there can be the slightest link between what I feel about social iniquity and what I think of the origin of species.

Totalitarianism: intellectual racism. Thought's unintermixed offspring, with all the bad consequences of genetic homogeneity.

In our present ignorance of humanity's moral needs, better vary its diet as much as possible, lest it be deprived of indispensable vitamins.

Had certain philosophic works, which might well be described as glorious cathedrals of error, never existed, I should deeply regret it.

Don't sacrifice everything to the idea that at the moment seems best and most efficient.
Progress often comes from a return to the rejected.

Peril of intimate notebooks. One neglects the most common, the most customary, to make way for the unusual, the adventitious.
One is silent about the things one lives by: which go without saying.

Habit of studying oneself as though under a microscope. One accepts a vagueness of the whole, in order to be precise about minute details.

Better look at oneself from time to time with a naked eye, in order to see oneself more accurately.

It is easy not to be too closely drawn to those who approve of us, but difficult not to withdraw too far from those who condemn us.

O truth—thou who art so fair with respect to things, so ugly with respect to men . . .

Among scientists who deserve to be called writers there are some who give much thought to writing well (Cuvier, Termier, Nicolle), and others who come by their style without seeking it, without wanting to, through the sheer power of emotion or thought (Pasteur).

Midway between, Claude Bernard.

Certain scientific writings are *literarily* irreplaceable because they express feelings peculiar to the scientist, and which he alone is qualified to express: emotion in the presence of new-minted truth, eagerness to communicate it to others, irritation at seeing it misunderstood, etc.

One also sometimes finds a specific emotion attached to the object of study itself: corpuscular emotion (Jean Perrin), astronomic (Laplace, Arago), biologic (Carrel).

Journal, essays, maxims . . . Differing methods of self-extraction.

Pleasure of research: raising nature's petticoats.

If a text has been reprinted many times, and has not been proofread by the author, typographical errors crop up. As do mutations in a species, when natural selection is defective.

Life-tension, possibility of pleasure.
All pleasure is life-degrading.

Like intelligence, stupidity may be only a reflection.

Pseudo-genius holds up better than real.

In an old work by the philosopher Caro, I come across a curious chapter on the *Examen de conscience nocturne*, by Francisque Bouillier, who was in certain respects a precursor of Freud, since he held that the dreamer was partly responsible for his dreams. In dream:
"The characteristics and passions of the waking state are limned as in a truthful mirror. One might say that in that state we are no longer ashamed of our vices or our dishonesties and that, along with shame, we give up the dishonesty toward ourselves that is so frequent in the waking state."
He says, further, that the sleeper teaches us to know the waking man better; from dreams we can get hints for the

therapy of the soul, as well as for self-knowledge and self-control.

No less striking is Caro's commentary: "It may happen that beneath the moral nature . . . there exists another nature of a very different sort, a primitive nature, if you will, tamed with great difficulty, still quivering and ready to spring up as soon as discipline is relaxed, an ensemble of bad instincts ordinarily held in check by reason, manners, and opinion, and which, as soon as these obstacles are weakened (as happens in sleep), rush past the lowered barriers, to take one form or other of insolent revenge. . . . It is not enough to say that dreams express our habitual life: they often explain as well that fund of half-unconscious reveries or desires, suppressed by reality, that move obscurely under the surface of our official, classified, defined existence. . . . Dreams, then, represent to the dreamer not what he is or has been, but what he would like to be and regrets not having been able to be by fault of circumstance. . . . In dream we are deprived of that power of inhibition or arrest which is so useful in ordinary life . . . and which, paralyzed in dream, opens the door to the most disordered fantasies." (From *Mélanges et Portraits*, 1888)

The unconscious, inhibitions, repressed desires: we aren't very far from Freudianism.

In areas where I can be partial without consequences, I make up for the effort at objectivity I impose on myself elsewhere.

Ideological falsehood.

I do not despise the scientist who falsifies or suppresses the truth in submission to a doctrine, but there is a quality of respect I shall no longer be able to accord him.

I have had to learn to mistrust those I esteem, a thing I should never have believed I should be asked to learn.

I admit that many things have changed for me since it began to become clear that an increasing number of scientists are acting in obedience to an imperative other than that of truth.

An interlocutor tries to catch me in an error of logic or a contradiction. Does he expect to make me uncomfortable? Is my satisfaction in thinking as I do as great as all that?

Since science began to have such great public diffusion, a scientific *"café du commerce"* has begun to spring up.

Seriousness is nothing but futility taken more seriously.

There is a goodly dose of refinement in credulity. Isn't it people of quality and good society who retail all those stories of sorcerers, water-diviners, and seers?

To deny all such stuff wholesale is to offend too many honorable witnesses.

Every fact is greater than one thinks.

The great scientist Lucien Cuénot once told me the story of an impassioned zoologist who, having lost his mind, invented and described in extraordinary detail precisely the animal he needed to illustrate his theories.

Delirium had created proof.

The researcher who stresses the importance of what he has discovered is thought boastful. If he does not stress it, people say he hasn't grasped its significance.

Renan: "Reforms never triumph directly. . . . They are a storm that pushes backward those who try to meet it head on." (*L'Avenir de la Science*)

Valéry: "We enter into the future backward."

I suspect there are few people who are asked, as I am, to give their views on things as different as: the miracles at Lourdes, the raising of frogs, the dangers of atomic disintegration, the style of Chardonne, the boners of Professor Benoit, the effectiveness of psychoanalysis, the transmission of acquired characteristics, the future of cybernetics, interstellar travel, the superman, levitating tables, changes in sex, astrology, parthenogenesis, the risks of intermarriage, the mechanism of evolution, the upbringing of children, etc.

Not to mention those who ask me about parakeet diet, turtle growth, the molting of falcons, the marriage customs of snails . . .

It is easy to say what one intends: the difficult thing, sometimes, is to have an intention.

What makes discussion with Marxists laborious is that for them no problem is sufficiently limited to warrant our examining it without bringing in the whole world-picture. Even if they were right about the whole, there would still be many cases in which one ought to forget the whole in order to seek a partial solution.

It would be easy for me to conclude that the Marxists have the gross social truth; but they take too much advantage of it to abuse the plain unqualified truth.

People want one to put oneself out for them: they would rather be feared than loved. I am always surprised by the satisfaction they feel in extorting what they know is unpleasant for us.

I like a writer to teach me something other than his talent.

My exclusions come neither from indifference nor from disdain.

I have removed almost everything from my life, and there still remains far more than I know how to make use of.

X. said: The more a work excels in a genre I happen to dislike, the more I curse it.

I am vaccinated against the begging form of vanity.

Contradictions in my thought?
Certainly, but many fewer than in reality.

Having nothing eye-opening to say is no excuse for the kind of talk that would make a man sleep standing up.

Every doctrine is rescued by its impurities.

We may eventually discover that it is more reprehensible to punish certain faults than to commit them.

"Did X. have good taste?"
"I don't know, but he had the sort that was bound to become *the* taste."

Atomic disintegration is engaged in making man to-morrow's fossil.

Style: to try—in spite of scruples—to maintain an easy gait.

A good partisan is not satisfied to make show of the indignation implicit in his role: he really feels it.

To choose between the absurdity of what surrounds us and the absurdity of what one would add in order to make it a little less absurd . . .

He who thinks as I do is empty for me.

No risk in opposing the moderates: they attack only with moderation.

Two styles of narcissism: either one tolerates no change in one's image or else one loves oneself even in caricature.

It is repugnant to me to see even an event I long for born of falsehood.

Submission to good taste is often facilitated by an absence of personal taste.

At long intervals a writer has the agreeable surprise of being aided by words: the obstacle becomes a springboard.

Satiation with beauty is not a healthy ingredient of taste.

Occasionally someone asks to visit "my laboratories." . . . And I am amused by this plural form for what scarcely deserves the singular.

The strange and slightly unhealthy taste for scandalizing oneself—for being "evil-minded" with respect to oneself . . .

I am sure Maupertuis was one of the first to think of subjecting the mind to "metaphysical experiments, stranger even than those that have to do with the body."

He wanted, for example, to discover how to stimulate dreams, to bring about hallucinations in those moments between sleep and waking, to study the properties of vision-causing potions. And also to experiment on the origins of the nerve systems and on the brain itself. "One might discover the means of curing madness."

"After the passage of so many centuries during which, in spite of the efforts of great men, our metaphysical knowledge has not made the slightest progress, we may believe that if any advance is possible, it must be sought by new means and as extraordinary as those I propose." (*Letter XXIII*, 1753)

Cerebral surgery, psychochemistry, research on halluci-nation-producing fungi, etc.: metaphysical experiments.

The partisan is quite sincerely outraged when one won't be taken in by his tactical tricks.

A pacifist is a man who has not yet met the cause that can make him put up his fists.

Vandel writes very justly: "Education is an embryological method which, rather than being practiced on the embryo, is used on children."
Alas, pedagogues too often practice induced teratogen-esis.*

I have an advanced grudge against the brash, for what I foresee they will extort from my weakness.

I like audacity in those who have everything to lose by it; moderation in those who have nothing to gain by it.

*Monster-birth.

213

People already know too much for their ignorance.

I would go far to avoid seeing certain things that most of my contemporaries pant for.

It is my intention to believe as little in chance as in Providence: no small undertaking.

I have never felt myself so much at ease in any intellectual position that I feared being dislodged from it.

According to the modern theory of "cosmo-analysis" (A. C. Blanc), the living species of former periods embodied, in a mixed state, a large number of characteristics and elements which "are resolved into more and more homogeneous and distinct entities by lysis and segregation of those characteristics which, in the primitive state, were mixed."

This idea may be found distinctly formulated in Renan's *Cahiers de Jeunesse* (1845):

"Syncretism of forms. Nature has not differentiated the organs. All is confused. Bird, reptile, etc., intermixed . . . The species were engendered at a period when they were still indeterminate, still syncretically confused: the system of those who reject classifications and species is false with respect to the present, but true for the past. (Always and everywhere the same laws—for the human mind, too: syncretism, differentiation.)"

See also *Souvenirs d'enfance.*

Since a vast number of people have become as though deaf to certain moral stimuli, appeal to the "universal conscience" has become illusory.

This does not mean that the deaf group is any worse than the other; but one must realize that when one speaks, one does so for oneself alone.

X. will not shake hands with Y. because the latter was a collaborationist; Y. avoids that of Z. because he approved the crushing of Hungary. . . .

The number of those who have not smiled upon assassins grows steadily smaller.

Shall I confess that I myself am outraged when I consider that, doomed as I am to rot tomorrow, I deny myself pleasures?

Between him and me there is a very small abyss. . . .

I am healthy enough, anyway, to condemn the sickliness I find seductive.

Languages common to all men: mathematics and erotics.

Vigny, Kafka:
"They know neither why they are in prison nor where they are to be taken later, and they know that they will never know. Nevertheless there are some among them who never stop wrangling to learn the history of their trial. . . ." (*Journal d'un poète*)

Francisque Bouillier devotes a long essay (*Nouvelles études familières de psychologie et de morale*, 1887) to the vocabulary of politicians and to "the deceptive euphemisms" their dishonesty makes use of.

In the advertising blurb that comes with a new medicament I note—among the symptoms it relieves—"various forms of pessimism." . . .
Another drug offers us mental health, "eudemony," "happiness resulting from an active life in harmony with reason." (*La Vie médicale*, 1958)

I have in me some scraps of certitude, but I do not know how to sew them together.

Remedies for fatigue?
It is protective: let strength remain inside the box.

I made my acquaintance with the majority of the great works of literature when I was adolescent and perfectly incapable of savoring them. Having had no time to reread them since, I judge them by memory, with the taste I have formed in the meantime.

It sometimes happens that I adopt an opinion without having had time to provide myself with reasons for doing so: I buy it on credit.

The laying season is over for the frogs.
Now I must wait for next year to recommence the studies that interest me.
This lends some compensation to aging.

Statistics teach that single persons have shorter lives than the married.
A humorist would remind us that the Negro slaves out-lived the freed.

Research: to start out from what one thinks one knows, and pull on the line in the hope it will break . . .

I am fettered by a thousand little obligations resulting from my independence.

It costs me something to refuse, and there is nothing, or almost nothing, I relish accepting.

There is almost never any merit in being good, but there is occasionally some in not being worse.

It is his animosity that causes his suffering. . . . Of course, but his animosity, in its turn . . .

To be very honest, I think there is nothing in the world as ravishing as a blue tree-frog. In this Amphibian, which is ordinarily green, the blue coloring results from a loss of yellow pigmentation. If all tree-frogs were blue, evidently the green would strike us as the masterpiece.

I have lived so long in contact with the essential that sometimes I find myself vaguely tempted by the accessory.

In scientific research, great ideas, intuition, daring, "genius," are far less operative than one generally supposes. But, on the other hand, very few people—other than specialists—have any idea how much finesse, ingenuity, "practical logic" (Senebier), adaptability to reality, imagination for detail, tactical flair, enter into the execution of a really good experimental program.

In disagreement with Oppenheimer, I do not think non-scientists are condemned in our times to ignorance of the great—always provisory—conclusions of science. What they are cut off from, rather, is having an opinion—bringing judgment to bear. Science may indeed be out of reach, but it can drop fine fruit to everyone.

To know how to recognize the human even in the inhuman. The ignoble is often poorly formed nobility.

Certainly our epoch is not altogether as hideous as it is barbarous. . . .

People never love truth so much as when falsehood reigns.

The incomparable fun of setting up a new experiment— of asking nature a question that has never before been put to her.
Never mind who has the right to interrogate that great lady: the event is marvelous.

I cannot help it: other people's merits stare me in the face.

It is allowable to wonder, alas, whether fanaticism, by the very operation of its methods, does not confer preferential survival in group competition.

Good faith, scruple, respect for man, etc. will perhaps be *lethal* characteristics tomorrow.

When evil has achieved a certain degree of power, it rallies to its cause all the friends of peace.

I should be curious to see who are to be the true men of genius formed by this age of false geniuses.

I put as much passion into boredom as into interest.

How do we manage to justify ourselves even in our contradictions?

Most men cannot be moved except by commands and ordinances; they submit blindly to the "deductions" of their party axiology.

I fear this abolition of the reflexes that comes of ideological intoxication.

These living systems were men when they chose the system to which they would give their allegiance; since then, they have become no more than automatons, corpses in service to that initial choice.

Incapable of cadaverizing myself in this way, were it even in allegiance to myself.

Consequentiality in our feelings may make it troublesome at times to have consequentiality in our ideas.

In 1947 I wrote in *Nouvelles Pensées d'un Biologiste**:
"The energy of the atom will be unleashed, people will travel among the stars, life will be prolonged, tuberculosis and cancer will be cured, but we won't find the secret of government by the least unworthy."
We have freed atomic energy, we are on the verge of getting to the moon, we are curing tuberculosis. . . .

In politics my immediate reactions sometimes run counter to my distant hopes.

One can never depend upon love—and yet it is on love that everything depends.

My career has nothing to do with my real course in life.

A real partisan does not like to throw light on the debate; he would lose allies.

My impression is that materialism is closed tight and that spiritualism opens on nothing.

* Later incorporated in the present *Pensées d'un Biologiste*.

Valéry: "The sea, forever rebegun . . ."
Hugo: ". . . This immense landscape
      That ever ends and rebegins before us . . ."
(From *"Au bord de la mer,"* in *Les Chants du Crépuscule*)

Virtually every human attitude has something in it that repels us: who, indeed, is worthy of being severe? Or merciful?

My Godlessness is no less mysterious than your God.

The more a conscience improves, the more it does without crime.

Renan and Teilhard de Chardin:
"Is this game worth the trouble? Or are we dupes? A question scarcely formulated in man's heart, accustomed as he has been for hundreds of years to 'carrying on.' But a question the mere murmur of which, already perceptible, infallibly heralds coming thunders. The past century witnessed the first systematic strikes in the factories. The coming one will surely not end without certain *threats of strike* in the noösphere. . . . The world's elements refusing to serve the world because they think . . . This is the danger." (Teilhard)
And in a letter to the Abbé Breuil:
"What an absurdity life appears to be! So absurd that

one feels thrown back upon an opinionated and desperate faith in the reality and the survival of spirit. Otherwise (if there is no Spirit, I mean), we should have to be imbeciles in order not to *go on strike* against the human enterprise."

Cf. Renan: "What would really not be unfair—what the workers ask of manufacturers—is that we be associated in the work of the universe as sharers of the benefits, that we receive at least some part of the fruits of our work. As things stand, although we share in the labor, we do not share in the dividends, we do not know whether any exist, and even our salaries are rather ill-paid. Others go *on strike*; we, all the same . . ." (From *Examen de Conscience*)

"Bees would stop working if they read in the papers that their honey was to be taken away and that they were to be killed as a return for their work. Man goes right on. . . ."

The desolating consolations of life . . .

There are certain writers whose simplest touches give food for musing.

One pities the man who falls down. But what of the upright man who keeps himself so with the greatest of difficulty?

Mystery of personal stylistics: a mere glance at a type-written page tells you—*visually*, and without your knowing why—whether or not it is possible that you yourself wrote it.

As futile to try to distinguish idea from execution in a scientific work—as to separate content and form in a literary work.

Curt thanks or late thanks.
Those who hurry to forget the favor, and those who prefer to think of it when its scar is healed.

I feel that I am in many respects a fossil—but a very living one.

What shall we have left if we are not allowed to exaggerate our needs?

To behave honorably toward certain opponents merely leads them to say that even the dishonorable have had to pay them homage.

Violent toward the violent, but not false toward the false.
Because you twist the truth one way it will not follow that I shall twist it in another.
Truth is not a hostage to be tortured by our quarrels.

Luck in research consists in discovering facts that resemble one's predilections.

Reason meeting with unreason produces effervescence.

Advantage of being on the side of the unjust: you will have them to stand up for you. And the others, as well, since the others are the just.

What mental decency it takes, if one cares for nothing, to form opinions which suggest that one does care for something.

Conflict between science and letters:
Literature can teach the truth, and the sciences can teach poetry.

Philosophic algebra.
To form an equation in which man does not cancel himself.

To write a few books in advance.
Then, if one died tomorrow, an extension of one's life.

The little renown I may have never loses any of its value for me, I admit, in view of all I have not done to acquire it.

I have never envied another man's admiration for someone else—only, sometimes, my own.

Certain literary talents make one think of those women whose splendor only emphasizes their misfortune.

"How can you live without believing in anything?" people sometimes ask me.

And you, I am tempted to answer, who believe in everything, how can you live the way you do?

I am no less inconsequential in despair than others in hope.

Nobody is readier than I to denounce the misdeeds of "capitalism," but I insist on being able to study a tadpole without being asked to reflect on class struggle.

One would long even more ardently for the abolition of social inequities, were it sure to result in the death of Marxist philosophy.

Barrès said merely that he would rather be wrong with his country, than right against it. Since that time, we have made progress: against one's *party* one can be nothing else but wrong.

I am daily more inconsolable to see the freeing of the masses linked to mental slavery.

The writers of "intimate journals" are fond of posing the problem of sincerity toward oneself. For me the question does not arise: in evil as in good, I feel only too strongly that I am myself.

The qualities that would make a work endure are not always the same as those that allow it to live.

I urge myself on as though I had perpetually to catch up with someone.

That which cannot belong to everyone cannot be life's essential.

No wound to pride can outlast a few minutes spent in *tête-à-tête* with my frogs.

I have lived so little that I sometimes have to rely on others for an opinion of life.

Believe in God? Like so many others I might answer: that depends on what one means by God. . . . But it seems to me a little dishonest to call anything one chooses God. The only specific property of God: prayability.

227

The wonders of instinct?
Those of intelligence astonish me more.

Soviet science: insults, falsifications, braggadocio of Michurinists.
If science everywhere were to follow suit. I should prefer to be a farm hand.

Dishonesty can't be learned.

It is always a piece of luck for the research worker to come upon facts that are worthy of him.

"The classics of Marxism have shown up Darwin's errors." (Lysenko) If nothing more than the "classics of Marxism" were involved, the charge would have no importance whatever. A scientist's errors cannot be criticized except by another scientist.

Michurinists.
My appetite for social justice won't let me accept their stupidities in biology, but their stupidities in biology can't stem my appetite for social justice.

They think I am defending Mendelian genetics: I am simply defending science against a faith.

It is horrible to see everything one detested in the past coming back again under the banners of the future.

Marxists.
Can they possibly be naïve enough to think that nature speaks no other language than the one it suits them to understand?

How unpleasant it would be to know in advance the style of future truths!

Michurinists.
If only they were the least bit right, what ineptitudes we would have to prepare to hear!

Even were reason to give us *carte blanche,* we would be prevented from conceiving a world that could satisfy us.

Chastisement in the beyond.
An infinite punishment would be terribly disproportionate to the fault; a finite one would be insignificant.

There is no black in nature, say the painters. In human thought there is death.

229

It requires little courage to keep pursuing one's course. It is in order not to lose heart that one persists in moving on.

"A man who does not subscribe to dialectical materialism, to Marxism, will be less embarrassed than a Marxist if he chooses the first theory." (Aragon, *Europe*, October, 1948)

If Marxists *can be embarrassed* by any given aspect of the truth, we can predict, with perfect certainty, that they will be.

How could one fail to be embarrassed in research, if one were at all open to embarrassment by any discoverable thing?

Mendel's theory is "a monk's theory," says Aragon.

In that case it took a monk's mind to create the science of heredity.

I should rather see politics enter into the selection of scientists than into the selection of hypotheses.

An absurd dogma is perhaps less dangerous to reason than a reasonable dogma.

Those astrologers of science who dare predict the countenance of truth . . .

I respect truth even more since there have again come among us men who do not prize it above all else.

One has no right to be right except with the facts at one's command.

The only thing a dictator cannot dictate is truth.

Herbert Spencer compared human knowledge to a sphere which, by continuously dilating, should thereby increase its surface contact with the unknown. A defective image, because, insofar as science achieves general and simplifying relationships, one can say it reduces the surface it presents to the unknown.

Those who say of such and such a great man of learning that he would have been greater had he been a Marxist remind me of Lessing's pronouncement that Corneille would have written better plays had he been an Aristotelian.

I should never trust a system into which all the facts could be fitted—nor should I think any better of one that couldn't admit them all.

Humanity—too immature to be enclosed in the cara-
pace of a system.

Some researchers profit by the guidance of a system;
others by freedom of approach. Best not to deny oneself
either.

All one can hope from a system is that, with the truth
it embodies, it will repay us for that which it excludes.

The doctrines of philosophy will all break their false
teeth on the tough realities of science.

Never ask the truth whence it comes or where it goes,
nor above all—as one might about a crime—who is to profit
by it.

I am grateful to certain mistakes for reminding me of
the poverty of my truth.

Among the attractions of scientific truth is the unex-
pectedness of its consequences, and the fact that it often
turns against those who try to use it for their own ends.

Don't throttle truth. Once that is done, you can't re-
enthrone her.

Humanity, in its early infancy.
It is when a child plays at being a man that he seems most childlike.

The truths we cannot speak help us to speak the speakable ones better.

Because it is so pleasant, there is never much merit in speaking the truth.

Peril of the master idea.
When Goethe derives all the plant organs from the leaf, he is in touch with a very fine truth. But he meets with error when, using the same approach, he tries to derive the cranium from the vertebrae; and falls into the absurd when he makes shadow the source of all the colors.

"A system-grinder hates the truth." (Emerson)

The most the proponents of a system can say in its behalf is that theirs is at the moment the least harmful of the opposing claimants. But if human thought has progressed, it is because it has never at any moment of its history allowed itself to be ruled by lesser errors.

Measure and dishonesty. I prefer the man who refuses to read the thermometer to him who falsifies the reading by a tenth of a degree.

"State science gives the cue to State religion." (Victor Hugo, *Post-scriptum de ma vie*)

The pretentiousness of the human animal, wanting to think beyond his brain . . .

Why should the true be beautiful? The fact that it may be so argues no necessity.

The same instinct for life keeps the unbeliever at a distance from despair, and the believer from sainthood.

Life, that solitude—but what if no company exists? That prison—but what if there is no free space? That illusion—but if there is no reality?

Nothing is serious for the mind; for the heart, anything may become so.

It often displeases us to find our opinions espoused by others; they are shorn of all that makes them acceptable to us in ourselves.

The further I advance in years, the more I narrow the field in which I consent to exercise my judgment.

Having seen a certain amount of history in the making is a fact ill-adapted to reinforcing my faith in history.

In order to explain the evolution of species, certain biologists invoke mysterious directive causes. Transcendence for transcendence, miracle for miracle, much as in the "successive creations" of d'Orbigny . . . What is the point of bothering with the supernatural merely to make it work in nature's way?

It seems to me that if I were a believer I should give up the "micro-miracles" and keep only the "macro-miracle" which the universe may be.

Nobody any longer doubts that material means—brain surgery, hormone injections, and other chemicals—can be employed to produce profound changes in thought, in character, in the whole man. The public is as much upset by this as though the problem of liberty were being posed in a new way. Is it possible that people still believe the mind independent of organic conditions?

Expression would do well to take advantage of the rare moments when sensibility happens to be lined up on the side of reason.

235

If the partisans of human liberty had any approximate idea of how much must unquestionably be ascribed to determinism, one doubts that they would fight so hard to save what is left.

Impossible to decide whether we totally lack the essential or whether we already possess it by the mere fact of knowing that there is nothing essential to be found.

"The wicked man is merely a robust child." (Diderot)
And man grows more robust each day without maturing.

The abnormal, in art, is an extremely inexpensive method of disorientation.

What offends me is not that I should be ranked below X., but that anyone would doubt that I should be the first so to rank myself.

Lines of Victor Hugo's poetry revised by Sainte-Beuve . . .
We should be horrified were we allowed to see ourselves corrected according to the taste of our betters.

Disarming naïveté of an eminent thinker in the field of occultism . . .

Philosophers are better able to define a word than to weigh the value of a fact.

I sometimes wish that by the moderation of my life I might somewhat correct whatever excesses there may be in my writings.

Amiel in his *Journal intime* confesses that he longed to be an Albert Rilliet. . . .

They say: "Since we know nothing, let's leave the doors open to all possibilities."

So be it; I won't object—but on condition that you don't plan to make some sort of affirmation spring from a freely assumed ignorance.

I don't mind their opening up our lacunae, provided no one tries to fill them with dreams.

"Man is incapable of conceiving a God he would wish to resemble." (Villiers de l'Isle-Adam)

A State made up of statified men: an abstraction of abstractions.

The gentle release that age brings. One no longer fears the murmur of humankind when one knows there is little time left in which to hear it.

Injustice would be a slight matter were there not, in addition, all that it justifies itself by.

People sometimes complain of psychoanalysis for making men more resigned to injustice; and it is true that insofar as it makes the individual more normal, more receptive, more adaptable, and removes the neurotic element from suffering, it can work against legitimate revolt.

One might go so far as to maintain that we ought to leave human beings in bad shape as long as society continues to be so.

He who claims to love all things has no notion of what is involved in loving just one.

If determinism had been rigorously demonstrated at the level of microphysics, and if "relations of certitude" had been established beyond contradiction, I doubt that the partisans of freedom would, even so, consider the problem resolved.

Indeterminism.

I do not think there is the least relation between the indeterminacy of the electron and the freedom of man.

The soul gains nothing from a margin of contingency in matter.

Marxism.

For a weak and prideful mind, what seductiveness there must be in a doctrine that permits one to make decisive judgments on matters in which one is ignorant!

Certitude, servitude.

Nausea brought on by the "political," as by a spice cooked into every dish, giving them all the same taste.

Human progress.

No one can at this moment be sure he will not someday be tortured for his way of thinking.

By dint of butting against certain problems, the mind forms something very similar to calluses.

Eugenics.

Beethoven was hard of hearing, to be sure; but we must certainly not, on that pretext, refuse to reduce the number of deaf persons.

Perils of good sense and excessive reasoning: Voltaire does not believe in fossil shells, in the regenerative capacities of the fresh-water polyp, in animal grafts, in queen bees . . .

To predict oneself is to falsify oneself.

It appears that human intelligence faces man with problems he will certainly be prevented from resolving by intelligence alone.

The most appalling "what's the use?" is the one uttered by the man who has acquired the best of everything.

Weakness.
I sometimes think it would amuse me to be the object of one of those high public consecrations which would in turn allow me the nauseous pleasure of seeing people alter their behavior toward me.

The conviction of being right which is, in my eyes, the infallible sign of error.

I used to think a scientist was always one who sought the truth, whereas he is really often a man with his eye on a job.

Writers differ most, perhaps, in the quality of their mediocrity.

As one adds to the burden one carries, life (of which one asks less) grows lighter.

The yellow Colias, herald of fine weather. As soon as he appears one can be certain that the toads and the newts are on their way toward the ponds.
A single yellow butterfly makes spring.

I, who am so inattentive to human affairs, am agog at everything that has to do with animal life. I stop to listen to the stridulation of a cricket, to watch a carabid beetle cross a road; I wait to see a Cetonia fly off after unfolding its wing sheaths; my eyes follow the swing of a flower head bent by the weight of a bumblebee.

Innocent beauty of life. The restful joy of watching these anonymous masterpieces that speak to no one, expect nothing, look for no praise . . .

Works without afterthought, without intention, without aim, free of the taint of exhibitionism that spoils all human productions.

It is true that I scarcely know the Louvre, I do not frequent either the museums or the cathedrals, I have little interest in the loftiest creations of art. I am ignorant of almost all the things that excite the enthusiasm of connoisseurs. .... But you—do you know the eyes of the stone fly, the belly of the Copris beetle, the wings of the Calopteryx?

The beauty of life can take every liberty; it is not bound by the limits of taste.

There is no less of the unknown in a grain of life than of energy in a grain of matter.

If you could plumb the secret of this caterpillar, you would know more about yourself than all our famous doctors: it stands witness for something unqualifiable, something that does not figure in our philosophies.

Listen to silent nature. She alone is incapable of lying.

Better look more closely at what surrounds us than distract ourselves from it by pursuing novelties. I have never been very curious about exotic fauna or flora: there is more than enough in my own little garden to carry me away.

Mysterious splendor of living things. Inimitable, unintelligible, unpossessible beauty . . .
To love is to be unable to possess.

Beauty at once so strange and so brotherly—kin of the eye that takes it in and the mind that marvels at it.

Each one of all these tiny beings: like us—unique, and repeated *ad infinitum.*

Firsthand creation, creation in the pure state. Behold our source. A freshness welling up to us from the depths of the centuries.

The irregular regularities of life, the imperfect symmetries, the artisan awkwardness.

Familiarity with works of art disqualifies us for decently responding to those of nature.

To clean one's eyes of all human aesthetics.
To forget Van Gogh when one looks at a sunflower.

I find animals more moving than plants; embryos more moving than adults.

243

A lily is not soiled in my eyes—quite the contrary—by the presence of the asparagus beetle clothed in her droppings.

Beauty of the pink vermin that swarm in the bellies of the Geotrupe beetles.

The least remnants of a thing that has lived retain the nonpareil stamp, keep the brilliant signature: a fragment of tarsus or antenna, the debris of a wing sheath, wing dust, bits of shell.

Vital beauty is infused into every product of the living: coverings, webs, cocoons. . . .

Even the leaf swellings caused by mites have their own sort of charm. They still represent life, and even doubly, since they are life modified by life.

Life remains harmonious even in its disorder.

Too much brilliance in the living object can hide the dumb beauty native to all living things.

Has a naturalist any need to live for himself? He lives, by procuration, on the whole of nature.

What a profession it is, this daily inhalation of mystery!

Every Cetonia has its gold.

Walking gently through the grass, careful not to tumble the small Coleoptera clinging to the grain stalks, watching bees turn mauve when they explore yellow corollas, marveling over a fly with a green gleam that one has never before seen, stroking an old wall all carpeted with sporogonia, letting one's eyes follow those floating matches, the blue dragonflies . . .

I haven't yet grown used to the existence in nature of objects as gorgeous as the alpine Rosales or the cerulean Hoplite.

Visual gluttony induced by the quality of the living substances: the porcelain of the tree frog, the alabaster of the toad's belly, velvet of Trichia, coal of Staphylinus.

The pleasure of savoring nature is one of the few pleasures to which we always feel we have a right.

Life revealed by the beast.
The human in man disguises the living.

Are we authorized praisers of the beauty of natural things?

All we can do is to observe that nature, when the human eye is added, forms something very stirring to man.

245

Knowledge acquired through love will not harm love.

To polish one's style is to pretend that one has done better thinking than is the case.

Pacifism?
I have no wish to bleat with the wolves.

Nothing is more futile than the great debates of biological philosophy: the origin of life, the evolution of species, finality. . . .
We know nothing, and we shout ourselves hoarse for the sake of errors.

To achieve universal acknowledgment by means of what is exclusively one's own.

I am enormously fond of wasting my time, but by myself.

I cannot finish a page unless I feel it is already under the reader's eye.

Truth doesn't pay.

At sixty I am as thrilled by the discovery of a mutation in toads as I was at ten by the arrival of a splendid new toy.

Anticipatory narcissism: to love oneself, not as one is at present, but as what one hopes to be.

The fact that X. can have written such a good book is enough to disgust one with literature.

We must expect of chance that it will furnish us our thoughts.

X., that missing link between pig and saint.

Sour grapes in reverse.
When it falls to someone else, we are much impressed by a success we should scorn if it were our own.

That writer, I agree, has every pleasing quality—and the fact is, that I prefer almost anybody else.

A good day is one in which the past has kept fairly silent, those I love have caused me no anxiety, I have begun an experiment, set down a few reflections in my notebook. If, to top it all, no bothersome intruder has come to collect his tithe, then things have gone really well.

One must—they say—choose between capitalism and Communism. I will wait for reality to offer me something choosable.

For almost a year I have scarcely emerged from my garden. I want nothing from outside. I should make a good prisoner.

It is no easy business to manage one's modesty well.

Once trampled, truth is very slow to rise again.

If there is to be no State lie, there must be no State truth.

Poor algebraist.
I don't know how to resolve equations of which both terms contain human suffering.

When my aquariums are full of frogs about to lay their eggs, metaphysical torment takes a holiday.

I see so many people whose minds are confused that I am likely to end up by taking pride in the fact that mine is almost clear.

People will forgive a man everything except not dining out.

If we knew what literature is, we should by the same token know what life is.

Scientific error may be fertile—but only if it is not the rule.

I lose interest in the book I have just published. Like those fertile animals in whom parental concern is reduced to a minimum.

My astonishment in learning what certain critics single out for praise: if that is what they call "profound," I consent not to be so in their eyes.

Never forget that, in any case, tomorrow we shall all have been wrong. . . .

I have ended by acquiring a lasting sense of the ephemeral.

It is well to have in reserve some good reasons for taking death's side.

Sometimes we envy the other fellow the importance he manages to give whatever happens to him.

The reason why a thought came to us is often more interesting than the thought itself.

Carpe diem . . . No: *carpe minutam.*

There are certain effects in art that can't be had without a touch of vulgarity.

There is nothing like the conviction of acting for the good of humanity to make us completely inhuman.

If a man kills through egoism, he kills little; if through ambition, much; if by idealism, vastly.

To hope that others are less nauseated by us than we ourselves are . . .

Old age? What could it take from me? . . . I should have to be weary, indeed, not to be able to walk about my garden with a little notebook.

If a man born of germ plasm altered by a biologist were to commit a crime, who would be the guilty one: that man, or the biologist?

Each insect has its own hour for visiting the golden sheaves.
Eleven o'clock: hour of the syrphids.

There is a certain amount of cheating in a solitude that receives, through books, the best of society.
As though a bee were to receive the honey of the hive at a distance.

My great memories are worthless except to me.

Better not be too sure of the point one wants to make; one is apt to cut things too short.

No truth should be favored above all the possible truths.

251

My disdain for public opinion has become such that I am perfectly indifferent to its thinking too well of me.

In comparison with almost everyone else I feel pure, very pure—*purissime*, as we say in chemistry. And there is no merit in my being so, given the life I have chosen, the goals I propose.

The things that would tempt me are not among the attainable.

I am repelled similarly by those who are steeped in their bourgeois truth and those who are steeped in Marxist truth.

I hear the words of only a very few people; all the rest is background noise.

Metaphysical anguish is even worse for those who believe in total death, and therefore think that nothing will ever be explained, unraveled, allayed.

Waiting for things to come to us.
Sometimes they come too late.

If I had to account to anyone for my scientific or philosophic opinions, I should prefer never to open my mouth again.

I have not yet forgotten enough to have memories.

Marxists.
The great men of whom they boast—one shudders to think what they would have made of them had they been able to expurgate them as they pleased.

Objectivism, cosmopolitanism, deviationism: they make a crime of everything I admire.

There are a great many people whom I should be tempted to ask before listening to them: is it you who are about to speak, or are you planning to play me a propaganda record?

When I admire a book, it means I have found in it some sentences I can chew on.

There is still enough of the unknown in nature so that one has no right ever to call anyone an imbecile.

Vanity acquires no wrinkles.

If I resent animosity from those I care for, it is because it shows that they are unsatisfied.

Scientific research. It is all too easy to make an excuse of insufficient financial support. It did not cost anything to discover penicillin, to establish the chromosomal theory of heredity by crossing vinegar flies, to produce traumatic parthenogenesis in the frog, to transplant embryonic nuclei in the egg, etc.

Racial falsehood and racial truth.

Do not believe that there are superior races possessed of special rights, but know that race is a stable thing, and that even after thousands of centuries, under no matter what environmental conditions, it will keep its genetic patrimony unchanged.

What scientist would not long to go on living, if only to see how the little truths he has brought to light will grow up?

Incognito is a habit of the future.

"Nature" and "nurture," said the English biologists, to designate heredity and milieu, the two factors of the living being.

La Fontaine had got there before them with: "But the varied food strengthening in one his happy nature . . ."

254

Nature enchants me most when she seems least eager to please: I prefer moss to flower, frog to bird, dung beetle to butterfly.

What I care for in nature is what is least art.

Science: in action never proud enough; in understanding never quite humble enough.

Marxists.
They think that nature shrinks from chance, as the physicists of former times thought she abhorred a vacuum.

It may be that our science is, occasionally, bourgeois— but theirs is all the time Marxist.

Facts laugh at orthodoxies.
Nature is unorthodox.

Certainly belief is not always a weakness. It would be one in me.

Psychic research, astrology, occultism of every sort, etc. I am said to be too hard on all those things. But it is so

seldom I am sure of being right: I have to take advantage
of my meager opportunity.

Don't confuse sectarianism with intellectual policing.

Stupidity blows where it lists. . . .

The trouble with ideological monism: monotony of diet
—so say the physiologists—is bad for the functioning of the
digestive system.

I should devote less passion to the study of nature if I
could believe we were already in possession of her laws.

Marxists.

Without knowing anything about the universe, they
make it as bothersome for us as if we knew all about it.

To write a book, at last, that would be so much myself
that I should be tempted to recognize myself in it, and thus
have nothing to desire! If you don't like it, so much the
worse for me—or for you.

The whole of Oriental wisdom comes to no more than
a better management of sphincters.

Certain minds take on all forms of stupidity, just as certain materials gather all kinds of dust.

I am more convinced of being right through the way I live than through the way I think.

It is much less serious to go astray than to imagine one has hold of the thread that makes straying impossible.

Marxist science.

It is interesting to note that, in their view, the three great founders of biology, Mendel, Darwin, and Pasteur, were ridden with bourgeois idealism.

A little more in this vein and they'll convince us that the bourgeois intellect is the best equipped of all to penetrate nature's secrets.

When anything succeeds in spite of them, their only recourse is to "Marxify" it later on.

Judging by the way things are going, I foresee that we shall soon be told that certain scientific errors are more valuable than the truth.

I have too much respect for the masses to admit that one can serve them by talking nonsense.

I need nothing, but nothing would not be enough.

There are moments when, in order to go on living, a man is forced to appeal to the worst he has in him.

Death of a friendship—time's legacy.

The best of science is not necessarily the most efficient. Up to the age of the antibiotics—or, at least, the age of Pasteur—it is rather likely that the "healers" did more healing than the doctors.

It's a sad age when one feels like congratulating a man of science for not having betrayed truth. . . .

The past—the death no one can take away from us . . .

I am inclined to judge a belief quite differently, according to whether it asks the right to be one or insists on being the only one.

If one has to walk in line with idiots, better be in front.

In my dreams I often compose imaginary animals. Such frogs, such insects as I have come to know in sleep! Only last night I had in hand a bizarre creature: a giant bee with deep blue wings and a body trimmed with curly fleece. I took it in my hand, utterly happy to have discovered a unique specimen, and felt the cool dampness of its abdomen.

I suppose many naturalists must similarly dream themselves fabulous menageries.

The persistence of an opinion proves nothing in its favor. Astrologers still exist.

He who has believed, will believe. . . . But possibly not the same belief.

There are a great many words of which, as one goes on living, one learns no longer to know the meaning.

What a good life it would be that could, without the expedient of despair, reconcile us gently to death.

It is not life I reproach; it is my life.

It is not my life I reproach; it is life.

259

I don't trust planned goodness.
There is quite enough good to do without being good.

Christian charity stops at the pantry door: anyone who works for wages ceases to be our neighbor.

I freely recognize that I am sometimes as dishonest as is conceivable in a person who has, once and for all, decided that he would be honest.

I sometimes wonder what the prayer of an atheist might be.

The only answer sometimes to be made to a contradictor: "Study the question for forty years and then come back to see me."

Petitions, appeals . . .
It is painful to have to refuse to sign something one may believe in more sincerely than the majority of those who sign it.

The atheist's flashes of doubt may have just as high a worth as the compact certitudes of the believer.

Life compels us to water our wine.
Let us secretly lay aside a few unbaptized drops.

When one knows another person deeply, one usually
has no difficulty in seeing what he is really called to do in
life—what tasks, demanding his effort, privation, renunciation, self-extension.
These, however, are not usually the ones he chooses for
himself.

What I feel toward this writer is massive rather than
great admiration.

I try, in writing, to hit *my own* jackpot.

The work of science prolongs that of nature. *Gesta na-
turae per scientiam.*

One can sometimes say: "It's too much." . . . But how
could one ever say: "It's enough?"

The odious part of dishonesty is that it ends by giving
honesty bad conscience.

If Communism is a religion, try not to be its Monsieur
Homais.

Why wasn't that honor conferred on me?
First: Because I have not done all that's required to merit it;
Second: Because I have not done all I would have had to do in order to get it without meriting it.

Satisfaction of having discovered a few small biological facts.
I have such passion for truth that, even when it is very humble and comes from me, I am enraptured by it.
If a research worker did not put the truth above all else, one would have to ask why the devil he ever chose such a profession.

The only things that could arouse my desire are ones that I have no desire to do.

Rare are those beings with whom one could enjoy being indignant.

Ambition . . .
A soap bubble wanting to be a little bigger at the moment it is about to burst.

Of those who "know how to keep afloat" the most unpleasant are the ones who seem to be unaware of their water skills.

Ought one to complain of or pay honor to a belief that stupefies so many eminent men?

The terrible word "happiness," which one cannot even murmur without unleashing a tumult of regrets and fears . . .

Intellectual freedom, respect for man, love of truth . . . Let no one expect me, as I approach the end of my.life, to renounce the few ideas I have lived for.

All one has to do in order to lose courage instantaneously is to imagine the hour of one's total fulfillment.

God as "flaw."
The whole problem is to know whether we really want to deify the gap in what we know.

"If we suppress scruple in knowledge, what will be left of science?" (Nietzsche)

If I am to trust a man's esthetic sincerity, he must not make show of more taste than he has the right to.

It is clumsy of a writer to let us see what he prizes most in his own work: he makes criticism easy for us.

Those mountainous good deeds that bring forth mice . . .

Less and less do I know what man is; but in this increasing ignorance less and less do I find any approach to God.

We admire a beautiful flower without asking whether it owes its beauty to good soil or to an opportune shower. . . . It is perhaps not otherwise that we should admire a moral act.

Every man has a right to the torments provided by leisure.

The curtain is beginning to come down, and I am just at the point of asking myself whether it is going to rise. . . .

A certain charge of stupidity seems necessary for getting off to a start; after that, one can let oneself become more intelligent.

The world belongs to the superior second-raters.

Those we love, even if they disappear, do not hold our love.

It must be admitted that one is almost always enriched by what one worked hard to avoid.

I am less shy with people who come to visit *me*—like a dog that is bolder at home than outside.

The further I go, the less I know.

When people ask me if I work a great deal, I hesitate to answer: is it work to hunt earthworms to feed my toads? to empty my aquariums and clean my cages? to muse over a problem at night, or pause over the choice of a word?

One has to begin by having eloquence if one is going to "twist its neck."

Suffering begets ideology, which, in turn, teaches suffering a thing or two.

I should rather discuss biological questions with a breeder than with a philosopher.

Here and there in the course of my life I have probably been what is called "good," but certainly not in those moments when I passed for such.

Marxism.
They answer me: Soviet science has discovered this, invented that. . . . But I have never said that a man could not discover anything because he was a Marxist.

They tell me: You attach too much importance to this dispute that has put Soviet and Western biology into opposition.
But biology is a serious matter for me; and above all, it is one of the few fields in which I am qualified to judge the repercussions of dialectic materialism.

What is true of the red frog is not necessarily so of the green or the dalmatina. And they say truth can be predicted from principles!

As soon as something has been discovered by a research scientist, it is sure to be quickly rediscovered by another: it is now known to be discoverable.

How much love is needed to forgive the clumsiness of love!

266

I am not one who likes to embark on long-term projects. From *now* until *then*, what calamities may be in store! One feels as though one were setting the stage for the coming drama.

There's not a word too many in this book; but isn't it the book that is superfluous?

Vanity has rapid digestion.

Let a dictator perform an act of good sense, and people immediately hail him as a genius.

The astounding complexity of science: radiation, waves, electrons, hormones, the sympathetic system, genes, D.N.A., the unconscious, Pavlovism, psychoanalysis . . . One is astonished that people keep their heads.
In point of fact, they do not keep them.

Light stimulates the secretion of a hormone which in turn acts upon the nervous system, which in turn . . . etc.

Doctor and biologist know less and less what they are doing when they handle a living being.

267

Jealousy between women.
I have never yet seen a man made ugly by looking at another man.

Harder and harder for a naïve reader to form an accurate judgment, since almost everything in literature has become repartee, malice, pastiche, allusion, calculation, bravado, compensation, supplement, risk . . .
One is in danger of taking an archaism for an innovation, a deliberate platitude for salient originality. . . .

Harmony of judgment between a layman and a connoisseur can be based only upon a misunderstanding.

Humbug of the occultists.
To these retailers of wonders, one would be tempted to say: the really extraordinary thing is that with so many people like you on earth, there should be such a want of the extraordinary to tell.

Certain of our friends, whose taste differs from ours, spoil our view out of kindness.

He who does not suffer more than reasonably generally has nothing very important to say.

268

Honors?

After a certain age one shrinks from modifying one's "body image."

I am very much afraid that most of those who reject Communism do so for the very reasons that make it so painful for me not to embrace it.

I admit I am a demanding reader.

I expect of each new book that it will reconcile me with literature.

What I ask of a book is that it create the need of what it offers.

I have never wanted grist to be brought to my mill.

And above all, I try not to have any mill.

I haven't refused much in the way of honors. I have settled for not asking.

To come on a book in which one doesn't find every page sounding that note of coaxing: just see how sensitive I am —or smart, or cynical, or loyal, or insolent, or sophisticated . . .

269

To try to remain true, even in one's taste for truth.

The two impossibles: God as people conceive of Him, and matter as they think they know it.

Each individual sets his own thresholds of wonderment. Mine start with the animal world.
Explain the toad to me, and I won't ask you about man.

What is gained by narrowing the field of miracle? If a God can have slipped a soul into a monkey body, He can equally well have pulled man out of the slime.

The trouble with pseudo-knowledge, as with pseudo-food. It blocks the available "valences" for real nourishment.

"You have written this, which contradicts that . . ."
"What of it? I would never write another line if I thought I could be chained to it."

I am one who writhes like a snipped worm when I do not understand. . . .

I've seen people who act kindly, solicitously, who can be touched by pity, who try to attract love or good opinion, who hesitate to refuse or disappoint, people who do their duty or who devote themselves to earning a paradise . . . but I still do not know precisely what it would be to be good.

"In this vast unknown whose existence you acknowledge, in this immensity of the not-understood, and perhaps incomprehensible, why should there not be something a little less afflicting for the heart than what *you* think to be the truth?"
I do not listen to this voice.

When one has just finished tearing oneself to pieces, it is quite embarrassing to appear before others.

Art is brief, nature long.

We oversimplify the theses of our forerunners in order to credit ourselves with putting in the fine touches.

An artist must contrive to want his flaws.

Every death drives death into our heads.

To the biologist the birth of a soul would seem even more incomprehensible than its survival.

Every chagrin has its personal timbre. There are certain notes one does not perceive when they are covered by the great organ tones of grief.

In the midst of what is known as success, I cannot help feeling a sort of shame.

To be just toward the unjust—but making it clear that such justice is charity.

If, in order to hope, it were enough to know the extent of one's own ignorance, I should hope. . . .

This premium of pain that we must pay—to whom?

I have never felt the need of believing nonsense in order to fortify my thinking what I think.

There are no astrologers in the U.S.S.R.; but why is it that in the only country where false sciences have been abolished, true science is falsified?

The only persons who can save us from loneliness are those who can reduce us to it by their absence.

To each his own way of loving truth. One scientist will refer to the blisses of discovery; another to the torments of research.

Practical value, sign of truth.
I admire useful learning because it attests connivance with the real.

It is not acting upon things that matters, but demonstrating by one's ability to act upon them, that one speaks their language.

Man rejects all explanations *ad usum hominis.*

I do not believe in absolutely everything that I live by.

"Doubt is the most religious act of human thought." (Guyau)

In order to perform miracles God would have to pervert the law, like a charlatan.

One denies more than one should when one cannot believe as much as one would like to.

273

Death, life's only reality . . . In everything outside its jurisdiction imposture has too free a hand.

The virtuousness of instinct protects us against the shameless behavior of reason.

Metaphysical anguish.
Not the least of its disagreeable traits is that it cannot make itself explicit in a form admissible to reason.

I bear less grudge against the man who wrongs me than against the one who rebukes.

The smaller the field vanity has to feed on, the more voracious it is.

Talent may need a grain of vulgarity to give it body, just as perfume requires a grain of musk.

Not even a God could make me say "I know" when I do not know.

Consolation of the envious: maybe people don't dare to tell me all the bad things they know about that friend.

The peak of art in the comedy of life: to achieve being reproached for being what one pretends to be.

Too easy to "beautificate" on the great themes.

Humanity cannot be depreciated except by claims based on individuals who, in our view, have tainted the human profession.

"Literature is a diminution of all that it touches." (Renan)

When I hear the nonsense that falls so freely from the lips of incompetent persons, I am tempted never again to speak of anything but frogs.

Conscientious objection?
Don't ask the permission of human laws to give preference to divine ones.

All reality is good for us, on condition that we are given times to digest it.

The really great questions are those on which Tom, Dick, and Harry are no more likely to make fools of themselves than anybody else.

I do not see how even a God could take us, as we are, and make immortals of us.

I find it quite natural that X. does not admire me, but not that he misjudge me to the point of thinking himself bound to feign admiration.

It offends me when people pity the misfortune of those whose happiness they would not relish.

Praise according to body weight.
The heavier one grows, the bigger the dose one demands.

If people say they admire me, I smile, and doubt. But if they tell me they have come to love biology through my books, I accept, and am satisfied.

A superman could believe only in a super-God.

Even when I am convinced that a man is wrong I cannot help wondering whether his very error may not be directing him toward a truth whose existence I am incapable of imagining.

If there is a God, science is reduced to seeking the causes of the things He did not deign to create by miracle.

Copious, juicy, succulent nature . . . One would really have to be a glutton to want more.

Man can provide only partial answers even to his own preliminary questions.
How could he be capable of solving the problem wholly?

We know too much, today, to impute any part of our own intentions or desires to nature; but we do not know enough, and perhaps never shall, to replace those too human notions by something capable of satisfying us.

Certainly there is finality in nature, since there is finality in man's mind; but the problem is to know whether nature can "finalize" otherwise than through a cerebral cortex.

Suffering.
If there exists anything whatsoever that calls upon us to make ourselves worthy of it, it is through suffering that I shall have made my approach.

Incapacity for immobile contentment. What to do with one's winnings?

277

I intended to deal merely with an individual case, protests the writer. But would he have so intended if he hadn't counted on the insincerity of a fair number of persons, to pretend they saw the universal case in it?

The more mind one posits in the universe, the more one exposes it to the reproach of absurdity.

In the animal world one comes up against the mystery of life in its pure state.
All that's essential in man—without man.

In order not to believe the worst, one must feel in shape to endure it.

Don't cover ignorance with words: it is not an indecency in need of clothing.

One of the sure consequences of civilization is the enlargement of death's crime.

Goodness is impossible when one is not satisfied with oneself; and when one is, it is so easy that it scarcely deserves to be so called.

The attachments that can make us bleed when they are severed—are they the only kind?

The most precious treasure of all: to have put a good deal of suffering behind one.

"Mendelians" accuse the enemies of classical genetics.

"It troubles me that you should call those who have seen the truth of Newton's discoveries Newtonians. It is as though one were to call geometers Euclidians; truth has no party names. It is error that has a place for such partisan terms: sects have names and truth is truth." (Voltaire: letter to Clairaut, 1758)

The artist is the only man who knows what to do with beauty.

Since love exists in man's heart, it must follow—they say—that there is a source of love. Which is as though one were to say there must be a source of light because the glowworm has a light in its belly!

Marxists: I am terribly disappointed in the thinking of those who claim to know the laws of thought.

Believers: I am terribly disappointed in the love of those who claim to know the commandments of love.

279

So much the better if my truth can help another man to make himself another . . .

In a future age we shall be just as astonished to find that we have had politicians as leaders as we are, today, to find that we once had barbers as surgeons.

If anyone had told me when I was young that I would live to see true men of learning holding back what they knew to be the truth, in obedience to a political faith, I would not have believed him. Still less would I have believed him had he said that I myself would reluctantly retain some esteem for such men.

Bothersome letters: one compels me to look up a bibliographic reference, another to work out a courteous refusal, etc.

I am almost grateful to this good, insulting letter that puts me under no obligation at all.

I am only too glad to be shown the weaknesses of my opinions. In my view they have all too much strength.

Every pleasure is a *plaisir d'amour*.

How get used to the fact that people who are far from fools are capable of thinking the worst nonsense, that people who are far from liars tell the worst lies, that people who are far from monsters sanction the worst monstrosities . . .

I have an irrational aversion for the rationalization of the irrational.

With respect to the great philosophical enigmas, I have acquired a sort of negative reflex. More and more, I refrain from approaching them. Like a bird that quiets down for good after butting its head all too long against a pane of glass.

He who has made a fresh discovery for a while feels nature working with him.

Sterile arguments on the origins of things, on the meaning of life, on order and disorder . . .
I hurry to get back to my minuscule problems, to my counting of frog toenails.

I have not yet made up my mind—nor has anyone any more than I—whether man had or hadn't the right to be astonished at being what he is.

"Unity of belief, which is to say, fanaticism." (Renan)

Unsurprised disappointment of the reader, laying the book aside: one more fellow who knows no more than I about the only things it would be important to know!

It is difficult to speak of people one has known very well: one's memories are so compacted that they lack silhouette.

There is some point in yielding to others as long as one is still convinced one is right.

A lie can be less false than a well-chosen truth.

We resent our friends' knowing us so well, when they understand us so poorly.

The profit of loving comes, ordinarily, from loving the other less than ourselves. Contrarily, if we love more, nothing accrues.

The only thing we cannot do for a human creature is to make our heart beat faster when he is late.

Two sure things: one grows more intelligent every day, and one's love for those one loves increases.

It is always in what is dearest to us that we are stricken. As though the only crime were love.

Viewed from outside, all lives seem rather unworthy of being lived.

We owe almost everything that broadens or beautifies the lives of men to men who did not know how to live for themselves.

Few men are true enough to lie.

I am interested only in that which might be the property of all or can only be the property of one.

A fact generally proves most fertile while it is not yet understood.

Better always check to see whether the one further detail required by your hypothesis isn't qualified to make the whole of it superfluous.

When one reaches a certain age all is sullied but, equally, all is purified.

Those who play the game correctly.
Those who cheat but, if they are found out, accept their penalty.
Those who cheat, and protest indignantly against punishment. Among the latter, distinguish those who really feel their indignation from those who sham it, strategically.

I cannot help understanding the object of my indignation.

Consolation in time of suffering: there is far greater suffering ahead.

Liar—like one who thinks he possesses the truth.

Here's still another fellow who has discovered an explanation of the world . . . All the time they make me waste with their genius!

I should like to have the marble of certainty in which to house my doubts.

284

I see much more than man in nature, and much more than nature in man.

To seem satisfied with too crude a physics is to play into the hands of the dabblers in metaphysics.

In the presence of so many knowers, I feel more and more attracted to not knowing.

My truth does not taste good even to me.

I do not think that I have "lived"—but, to tell the truth, I find it difficult to understand what it would have been to "live."

Of the criticism of certain works.
A man brings a treasure and is reproached for not having wrapped it nicely.

It is one of the sad dishonors of our times that it permits falsehood to be maintained with honor.

I am a wise man without wisdom.

The people we describe as sensitive are often merely vulnerable through limited sensitivity.

A writer believes more firmly in a cause once he has found the right phrasing to express his belief.

I do not need to divinify those I revere in order to make my gods of them.

As for our understanding of the perennial problems, it is long since I've found in myself or elsewhere anything to revive my appetite.

People read so badly that an author could repeat himself indefinitely without their noticing. Such self-revision as one undertakes, then, is for oneself alone, and in order not to be one's own parrot.

Modesty: In all sincerity, I think people are out of their minds when they rate me at a thousandth of my own rating.

It may be a quirk of the naturalist, but I cannot manage to be more amazed at man than at his natural context. All the rest of the living creatures cause me such utter stupefaction that I have nothing left to add where we are concerned.

Some persons have concluded, from my repeated, insistent admissions of incomprehension, that I am headed for one brand or other of mysticism. "You are halfway there," they say. "Your 'I don't know' is going to lead to an 'I believe.'"

This merely proves that they haven't the slightest idea of the nature of a fine, clear, perfectly pure ignorance, with no ulterior motives.

If I were capable of accepting the answers of faith, should I not equally be able to agree to those of science?

Science, they go on telling me, brings you neither intellectual peace nor moral reassurance.

That's true: I lose—and want to lose—on all the horses.

Too easy to accept incomprehension?

One would hardly say so, given the very small number of persons who manage it.

I cannot conceive of a God, but still less of such a one as would make me regret not having believed in Him.

I am more of a misanthrope now than in my younger days, in the sense that I have almost always found man worse than I had expected. But my compassion has grown in proportion to my experience. Then that's what man is, this packet of horrors? Well, it could have been worse. . . .

A day coming to its end: one more that the void won't get.

I sometimes wonder whether reassurance can come from anything except the thing one fears.

Repulsive cheating: that of an artist of such capacity that he could have done without it.

In art and in morality, those on the "hither" side profit by the freedoms won by those "beyond."

Conciseness resulting from impatience. One is in a hurry to pocket one's pen again.

Hidden affinities between two writers prized by one reader. As between the very dissimilar plants favored by a single caterpillar.

I cannot say whether I am unsatisfied, because I am not quite sure what would have satisfied me.

Don't look too closely at an honest man—they say—if you want to keep your regard for him. Nor at a scoundrel, if you want to keep your contempt.

A writer is not always worthy of the quality of emotion he arouses.

Why should the evolution of the animal kingdom have been destined to terminate in man? No one pretends that that of the vegetables was fated to end with the oak.

Insufficiency of neo-Darwinism.

If mutations—which are the only variations in living things we know to be inheritable—seem incapable of explaining the evolution of the species, it is not because the changes they bring to the stock are too insignificant, but because they lack the necessary style or "curve."

The least human gesture is capable of revealing the whole course of civilization, whereas the mutation does not embody a resumé of the whole of organic progress.

We are still limited—as Darwin had it—to looking at human creatures "as a savage looks at a steamboat."

The whole problem of evolution must be contained in the tiniest step of life progress, just as the whole problem of literary creation in a single author's correction.

To know how to read between the species, as between the lines.

The evolutionary silence of nature as we see her.
It is undoubtedly an illusion to find less mystery in nature's current daily operations than in those of which she is no longer capable.

No philosopher juggles with ideas, no writer with words, as a juggler does with plates.

Artistic genius may consist in making the unacceptable acceptable.

Opponent? No: the man opposite me . . . And all I occasionally hope for from him is that he may give me the secret of thinking otherwise than I do. But, alas, contradicting me is not the same as knowing more about the subject than I do!

You will always have enough time to waste if you don't spend any on rubbish.

The hypotheses that try to force explanation are worthless. The lock opens easily if one has the right key.

A philosopher has less trouble finding good philosophy in the jokes of a buffoon than in the work of another philosopher.

Writing is itself a symptom.

No philosopher has ever guessed, predicted a single positive fact. Every time they have set themselves up to judge reality, they have been stunningly wrong. They are as though deaf to the language of nature. Why should we take their word for things in domains where error cannot be checked?

X. is so delighted to see someone else fall, that he refrains from trampling on him.
With a little urging he would pick him up.

Labyrinth.
To know the exit won't help in finding the path.

I am extremely utilitarian in the service of perfectly disinterested goals.

In Anatole France's judgment, Fabre was not a writer.
But Claude-Edmonde Magny finds that Anatole France was not one, either.

There are some problems that torment us to such an extent that we would be glad to see them solved, even by someone else.

Watch out, you are beginning to talk a little too much about truth. . . .

Man has some trace of original virtue.

There is no philosophic position that doesn't, in the end, produce a cramp.

I am poorly adapted to what I believe.

You have no right to think *this*, I am sometimes told, because you also think *that*. . . . A variety of objection that doesn't impress me. Although I am not very sure what I do think, I nonetheless trust it a little more than the prohibitions of your logic.

Try to cover the major part of the road together with your opponents.

I listen only to those who prove, or who move me.

What would happen to the notion of personality if brain-grafting were practicable upon man as it now is upon certain animals?

Should we see that all our law and much of our ethics depend uniquely on cellular properties of our nervous apparatus?

Science explains nothing, I agree, yet those who have tried to provide something better might as well have kept quiet.

Science or silence.

With respect to aesthetics, Kierkegaard has clearly expressed the theory of pedomorphism, or evolutionary progress, by means of infantile regression:

"In a general way, all true development is a return backward that leads us toward our origins, and the great artists advance by the very act of returning backward."

Man has good excuse for being irrational; nature sets him the example.

A philosopher has said: God will be. . . .

The biologist, considering present-day nature and finding little evidence there of forces which could have constructed God, would be more inclined to say: God has been. . . .

He who is not sustained by any faith must continually replenish his own light.

Don't hesitate to furnish your adversary with weapons, provided they are of good quality.

Better be as demanding in incomprehension as in comprehension.

By dint of predicting the future, they make it as annoying as a past.

Clumsiness of those who love us; if only they could, they would weaken their surest supports in us.

Never too late to understand.
I think that even on my deathbed I should sit up with interest if someone were to show me the solution of one of those old problems that have always baffled me.

I am surer every day that there is almost no love in man's heart, but am also each day surer that there is *some*.

Futile to use a high-precision thermometer to take the temperature of a phantom.

294

In adverse opinion there is almost always something to elevate, if not to alter, our own.

"The silent sensitivity of plants." (Schelling)

Don't behave irreproachably to him you love; it might make you see that he is not doing so in relation to you.

Science, said X., will always have the last word. If it is repugnant to man to be changed by chemistry, they will invent a drug to reconcile him with chemistry.

Since the invention of artificial insemination, we can no longer join Novalis in saying that every infant is "a love become visible."

Ask only for what men could not refuse you without lessening their own supply of it.

"Why are you working?"
"Trying to find a way of ending this chapter."
"And why the chapter?"
"To finish this book."
"And why this book?"
"To fill out the body of my work."

"And why your work?"

Here I hesitate in answering. . . . In proportion as the question broadens it grows more embarrassing.

I am all the more afraid of science because I believe in nothing else.

Seldom does anyone feel that stupefaction in the presence of nature's works which they deserve. Materialism, like deism, clouds our minds to the fabulousness of the real.

Organic evolution, from the virus to man: the unbelievable that has to be believed.

My illogicalities reassure me: I must still be alive.

Injustice may have something to gain by exceeding the limits: the excessive reactions it arouses give it a free hand.

A person too early cut off from the common interests of men is exposed to inner impoverishment. Like those islands which are lacking in some whole class of animals.

We should like to take advantage of all truth, without shutting our ears to a single falsehood.

"Direct view of the primary phenomena throws us into a sort of anguish." (Goethe)

Art must be a true falsehood, and not a false truth.

Beware the argument of continuity: if you give me the right to use it, I promise to prove to you that you are not alive.

If you refuse your own battle, you will be made a fighter in a cause that is not yours.

There is a certain kind of mental honesty which is perceptible only to honest minds. Which is to say, it goes unrecognized.

The longer humanity lasts, the further it advances in age and knowledge, the older will grow that *"même homme"* to which Pascal compared it—"that enduring man who lives forever and learns continually"—and the less will humanity be reflected in its young people, who will be unable to escape becoming more and more ignorant and ill-equipped by comparison with the accumulated skills and knowledge of the species.

The older humanity grows, the more it will need its old men.

Partisan lies.
If a doctor enters the battlefield, he removes his Red
Cross arm band.
If a man of science wants to tell a lie . . .

These gates, although always ready to jam, are
also capable of yielding to the slightest pressure, so as to
make us look like crashers of open doors.

One doesn't know for whom one writes.
Does one even know for whom one is?

Nothing easier than to throw dust in one's own eyes.

Too much trust: lack of talent for inner adjustment.
We do not struggle hard enough to maintain the firmness
of our opinions.

When I was young I pitied the old. Now old, it is the
young I pity.

Madness, the psychiatrists teach us, is often bound up
with an incapacity for love. Try to be as little mad as
possible.